D1075298

SACAJAWEA

Guide to Lewis and Clark

Sacajawea:

ILLUSTRATED BY LORENCE BJORKLUND

Guide to Lewis and Clark

JERRY SEIBERT

HOUGHTON MIFFLIN COMPANY
BOSTON The Riverside Press Cambridge

Contents

Library of Congress Catalog Card No. 60-13063

CHAPTER 1

A Sign from the Sky

It was very early one morning in the Moon of the Rushing Waters (March) a long time ago.

A clear flute-like call rang out high over the Rocky Mountains. Little Bear, a Shoshoni (*shoh shoh′ nee*) Indian boy, stirred in his sleep. Yesterday he and Eagle Chief, his father, had gone hunting. When it grew dark and the star people came out, they were still far from their village. They rolled up in their warm buffalo robes and slept on piles of sweet-smelling pine branches.

Little Bear listened as the high, silvery call came again. He was sure he had never heard it before in all his six snows (years).

"Look!" Eagle Chief was awake, too. He pointed far above. Against the pale dawn a long single line of birds flew north. The first pink rays of the sun tinted their great white bodies and powerful wings.

"They are the Great Swans — the Trumpeters," said Eagle Chief. "They must have rested nearby last night or their flight would be higher than we can see." Even as he spoke the huge birds soared up and up until they were only specks in the sky. "To see the Trumpeters is a good omen," he added.

The Indians looked for signs and omens in every unusual happening. Little Bear was sure these cloud-white birds brought a good message, but he wondered what it was.

He was still wondering, late that afternoon, when he and his father reached the brown, skin tepees of their village. Like all tepee villages it was built in a circle. A circle meant protection. It meant other things, too. The earth was round. The sun-chief who gave light and heat was round. The sky was as round as a great, blue, turned-over bowl. A circle was *strong* good-medicine.

Little Bear ran ahead. He was anxious to show Flower Woman, his mother, their fine bag of rabbits. But as he lifted the tepee flap he heard another strange sound — a baby's cry. He stared through the dimness inside the tepee. Flower Woman was sitting close to the fire with a cradleboard on her lap.

Little Bear was so astonished he forgot all about the rabbits he carried. Flower Woman saw them and smiled.

"You are a fine hunter," she said. "That is good, for now there is a new sister to care for. Come and see her, Big Brother."

Among the Shoshoni, a brother was his sister's protector as long as they both lived. Suddenly Little Bear felt very important. He ran to look at the baby.

Like all Indian babies, she was wrapped in soft skins and laced into her cradleboard. Her face was all Little Bear could see. It was a red-bronze color. Her eyes were squeezed shut. Her mouth was open — wide. A great deal of noise was coming from it. Little Bear was disappointed.

"She doesn't look like much," he thought.

Just then her dark, tear-wet eyes opened and looked straight into his. She stopped crying. He was sure she smiled. Little Bear felt taller than the tallest pine on the mountain.

"Already she knows I am her big brother," he said proudly.

"We must watch for a name sign," said Flower Woman. Names were a serious matter. They could bring good or bad luck. A boy's name was changed when he grew up. He might learn his new name in a "dream-vision" or earn it as a warrior. A girl usually kept the same name all of her life. Because names were so important, families watched for signs from the spirits to tell them what a baby's name should be.

"Father," cried Little Bear, "I'm sure the trumpeter swans were a sign."

Eagle Chief looked troubled. If the signs were read properly, the animal or bird a child was named for became its guardian spirit. Many girls were named for wrens and robins. These busy, hustling birds could help and guide them in the work of a squaw.

But the trumpeter swans flew beyond the places known to man. They flew higher than the mighty war eagle. They were as brave as warriors. Of what use would such a guardian spirit be to a girl? Eagle Chief sighed. Often it was very hard to read the signs of the spirits.

"We will go and ask Ka-wa-kan, the medicine man," he said. "He is the one to decide."

Ka-wa-kan's tepee smelled of strange herbs. Queer objects hung in the dusky shadows. Of course Little Bear wasn't afraid, but it was good to have his father close. Ka-wa-kan took their gift of two rabbits. He listened to Eagle Chief gravely.

"I must make strong magic to learn the truth," he said.

He sprinkled black powder on the fire. It burned with an eerie light. Blue-tinted smoke formed strange shapes as it floated up through the smoke hole.

Ka-wa-kan shook his turtle shell rattles and chanted. He stared into the fire a long time.

At last he began to speak in a faraway voice that made Little Bear's skin prickle.

"You saw a true sign," he said. "The Shoshoni are not as ignorant as the tribes of our enemies. We know the spirits may give great powers to girls as well as boys. There have been great medicine women among our people.

"It is right that the girl-child of Eagle Chief be named for the great swans," he went on. "They will be her guardian spirits. But do not call her Swan Girl aloud. Call her Sacajawea (*sak uh juh wee' uh*) — Bird Girl."

Eagle Chief nodded. One's real name was often kept secret to confuse evil spirits.

"Her guardian spirits will lead her moccasins," said Ka-wa-kan. He raised his left hand high and swept it down past his chest to show he was through speaking.

Little Bear was ready to burst with questions. But one did not question the medicine man. He told you all he thought you should know.

Until Sacajawea was a year old she spent

most of her time laced against the stiff back of her cradleboard. This helped her bones grow strong and arrow-straight. When Flower Woman was busy, she hung the cradleboard from a tepee pole or the limb of a tree. Sacajawea could see everything that went on and still be safe and out of the way.

When Little Bear was near, Sacajawea's sparkling dark eyes saw nothing else. She made happy little word-sounds whenever he came in sight. Little Bear, in turn, was sure she was the prettiest, smartest baby in the world.

When summer came, Sacajawea crept about on the grass near the tepee. One day she saw Little Bear sitting under a tree near the edge of the clearing. She crowed and gurgled to him, but Little Bear did not look at her.

Sacajawea started to creep to him. There were burs and sharp sticks in the grass. They pricked her hands and knees.

Sacajawea grasped the trunk of a small tree and pulled herself to her feet. Her lips were a tight, straight line. For a minute she swayed uncertainly. Then she put one wobbly foot in front of the other and started bravely off. Two steps and she sat down so hard her breath came out in a big "O-o-f!" A minute later she scrambled up and started off again. There were many falls before she crossed the clearing. Once she struck her head on a rock. She made a puckery little face, but she did not cry. At last she tumbled into Little Bear's arms.

"Ah-hi-e, ah-hi-e (I am very pleased)!" he cried. "My sister is brave and determined. She does not give up."

CHAPTER 2

A Strange Trail

Little Bear remembered the words of the medicine man. Sacajawea might need to know many things other girls did not. Who could teach her better than her big brother?

He taught her to swim as the braves did. She learned to slip through the icy mountain streams with hardly a ripple, and to swim with a heavy pack on her back.

One of the most important lessons a brave learned was to be able to tell always exactly where he was by day or night. It was a disgrace for a warrior to be lost even though he had traveled for many suns. More than that, a lost warrior's scalp might soon swing from an enemy's belt.

Little Bear taught Sacajawea to find her

way through the trackless forest and narrow mountain passes.

"Watch carefully as you travel," he said. "Remember landmarks — big things like the curve of a peak against the sky, and small things like the crooked branch of a tree."

"You are wasting your time," said the other boys. "A girl can't learn the lessons of a brave."

"Sacajawea can," said Little Bear. One day she proved it. They were a long way from home. Sacajawea had never been in this part of the mountains before. Little Bear saw an eagle's nest high on a cliff.

"Let us see if there are eaglets in the nest," he said.

"Eagles used to be Shoshoni people," he told Sacajawea as they climbed the steep cliff. "The spirits gave them strong magic so they could turn themselves into eagles. They flew high and far to watch for enemies. Then an evil spirit, from another tribe, stole the magic that turned them back into people. Eagles are still Shoshoni. But without the magic they can't become people again."

It was hard to find footholds on the steep cliff. As Little Bear crept along a jutting rock, there was a sudden sharp cracking sound. The rock went crashing down the mountain.

Sacajawea looked down fearfully. She could see nothing but grim, gray rocks. Suddenly she heard Little Bear's voice. For a minute she wondered if he were a spirit. Then she saw him lying on a narrow ledge part way down the cliff. All around him the sides of the cliff were straight up and down.

"You must go for help," he called. "There is no way for me to climb off this ledge."

Sacajawea worked her way back down the cliff slowly and carefully. The sun had set when she reached the valley. She stopped to study the landmarks carefully while there was still some light. Then she started off at a quick, steady trot. She wanted to run but she knew she would tire much faster if she ran.

It grew dark. The stars began their march across the sky. The moon floated above the peaks. Sacajawea had never been alone in the forest at night before. It seemed very quiet. The smallest noise seemed very loud.

The mountains made crooked shadows in the moonlight. Sacajawea stopped often to check the black and silver outlines that looked so different in the daytime.

Black clouds rolled across the sky and hid the moon and stars. It began to rain. Even the dark shapes of the mountains were blotted out.

Sacajawea huddled under a tree. The cold rain dripped through the leaves. An owl

hooted mournfully. It sent a shiver up her back. Was it really an owl — or an evil spirit? Close by, something crashed through the trees. Was it an elk — or a white bear (grizzly)? Her heart pounded. Even the bravest warriors were afraid of white bears.

Then she thought of Little Bear lying on the narrow ledge.

"Little Bear is depending on me," she told herself sternly. "I will not act like a baby."

As soon as the first pale light came in the east she started on. The sun was still high in the sky when she reached the village.

"I know the place," said Eagle Chief when she told him what had happened. "Eagles have always nested there."

He set off at once with a party of braves. They carried long rawhide ropes and rode their fastest horses. The next day Little Bear was home with only a few cuts and bruises to show for his fall.

"You traveled swiftly, Little Sister," he told Sacajawea. "It was a hard trail through strange country. No brave could have done better."

Sacajawea knew he could give her no higher praise.

CHAPTER 3

Wa-wo-ya-ka's Stories

When the Indians did not know why something had happened, they made up a story to explain it. Often they tucked a little lesson in. When children grew up, they told these stories to their children.

The history of the tribe was passed on the same way. Wa-wo-ya-ka (Storyteller) was the rememberer (historian) of the tribe. He told wonderful tales of gods and spirits and long-ago Shoshoni heroes.

All the children loved him. One summer day they asked him to umpire a ball game.

They played ball with long, curving sticks and a stuffed deerskin ball. The goals were stones piled at each end of a grassy field.

One team was named the Hawks; the other

was the Clouds. Sacajawea was a Cloud.

The teams lined up facing each other. Storyteller threw the ball high in the air. As it fell the Hawks pounced on it. The Clouds rushed forward.

Like the wind Sacajawea slipped into the circle of Hawks. She hit the ball with her stick. It flew down the field. Sacajawea raced after it and hit it again. A goal! The Clouds yelled with joy.

The teams lined up again. This time the Hawks stood firmly together. When the ball neared their goal, they whacked it back. The teams raced up and down the field. There were shouts of victory and shrieks of despair. Sacajawea darted through openings the others never saw.

"Truly her moccasins have wings," thought Storyteller.

Sacajawea was about to score again. One of the Hawks tripped her. She fell. Her stick bounced away.

"Unfair!" shouted the Clouds angrily.

"Poor losers!" jeered the Hawks.

Suddenly they were fighting. They rolled and struggled on the grass using fists and pulling hair.

"Enough!" Storyteller called firmly. "Let the game go on."

But when the teams lined up again, they glared at each other with angry eyes. Storyteller looked at their flushed faces and hateful frowns.

"Come," he said. "We will sit in the shade, and I will tell you a story."

"A long time ago," he began, "the Shoshoni were a mighty nation. They lived where the grass grows green and high. Their lands were filled with game. Even in the Hunger Moon (February) there was food in the tepees. No other tribe raised such fine horses.

"Other tribes envied the Shoshoni. They had to fight to keep what was theirs. But the warriors were brave and fierce. Always when they returned from war, it was a time of rejoicing. They brought back many scalplocks, horses, weapons, and prisoners. There

was great feasting while the tribe listened to their tales of courage."

Sacajawea's eyes shone. She felt as if she could see the mighty warriors. She could almost hear their comrades shout, "Ai! Ai! It is true!" as each man told of his brave deeds. Her heart beat fast with pride.

But Storyteller's voice changed. It became as sad as a moaning winter wind. "Strangers came from beyond the sunrise," he said. "Their skins were as white as spring clouds. Their eyes were the color of the sky.

"They had magic smoke-sticks that kill with thunder and lightning. They gave them to our enemies. Those tribes made war against us. Our warriors fought fiercely, but the magic smoke-sticks kill from farther than an arrow can fly. Again and again our enemies came. They killed our people and stole our horses. Finally we fled to the mountains.

"They cannot find us here. But each year we must go to the Great Plains to hunt buffalo. Without their meat and hides we cannot possibly live through the long winter.

"If we have pleased the spirits we soon find a big buffalo herd and kill all we need. Then we hurry back to the mountains.

"But if we have made the spirits angry, our enemies find us. Their magic smoke-sticks kill our warriors. If they find our camp they kill the old people and small children. They take prisoners. What terrible things happen to them we do not know. Those who are not killed or captured must live through the long winter without enough food or clothing."

Storyteller's eyes flashed. His voice thundered. "This would not be so if we, too, had the magic smoke-sticks!

"Now, my little ones," he said, "if you quarrel with one another when you are children you will quarrel when you are older. If we quarrel among ourselves our enemies will conquer us. We must be loyal to each other. We must be loyal to our tribe. Promise me there will be no more quarreling."

"We promise!" the children shouted. "We promise!"

"Some day I will help my people get the magic smoke-sticks," Sacajawea thought. "I will ask my guardian spirit to show me a way."

While they listened to Storyteller, the sky had grown dark, and thunder rumbled over the mountains.

"Why do we have thunder and lightning?" asked Sacajawea.

"It was this way," Storyteller began. "Long ago, there was neither thunder nor lightning. The rain fell softly as dew.

"One day Wa-gi-on (Thunderbird) heard the spirits praising White Arrow, Chief of the Shoshoni.

" 'He is fearless warrior and mighty hunter,' said one.

" 'He has never done a wrong,' said another. 'Always, he thinks of his people first.'

"Thunderbird was jealous. 'I will show them White Arrow is not perfect,' he thought.

"He changed himself into a bent old man and limped to White Arrow's tepee carrying a heavy parfleche (*pahr' flesh:* a rawhide leather case for storing food).

" 'I must go on a journey of many snows,' he told White Arrow as he put down the heavy case. 'All I have in the world is in this case. But it is too heavy for me to carry, and I have no one to keep it for me.'

" 'I will keep it for you,' said White Arrow.

"Thunderbird pretended to hesitate. 'Will you promise not to open it?'

"Usually White Arrow thought carefully before he promised anything, for a Shoshoni always kept his word. But this seemed an easy promise to keep.

" 'Yes,' he said. 'I give you my word.'

"Then Thunderbird went on with his plan. He kept the hunters from finding game. He kept the fish from the rivers, and the berries from the bushes. The Shoshoni grew thin and weak with hunger.

"White Arrow did not think of his own hunger, but he was sad because his people suffered.

"One night in a dream, Thunderbird whispered to him. 'The old man's case is filled with rich pemmican (a mixture of dried meat, berries, and fat). Think how good it would taste to the hungry children.'

"When White Arrow awakened, he longed to open the case, but he knew that he could not. He had given his word.

"Each day the tribe grew hungrier. The children were too weak to play. White Arrow could not sleep for thinking of their sad eyes and pitiful, thin bodies.

"All night long Thunderbird filled White Arrow's ears with the crying of the hungry children. At last he could stand it no longer.

" 'Why should the children starve when I know there is pemmican in my tepee?' he thought.

"He opened the case.

"Instantly the tepee was filled with swirling, beating, black wings. In the case were more young Thunders than there are flakes of snow in a winter.

"As they flew out they grew bigger and bigger. Jagged lightning shot from their eyes. Their voices roared until the rocks on the mountain were loosened and crashed into the valleys.

"Over the storm Thunderbird laughed and strutted across the sky.

"When White Arrow saw what he had

done, he begged the Great Spirit to put the Thunders back into the case.

"But even the Great Spirit himself cannot mend a broken promise. The Thunders were free forever.

"Now, when we hear the thunder roar, and see the lightning burn across the sky, we know someone has broken a promise."

CHAPTER 4

The Blue Bead Belt

A drum boomed in the Shoshoni village.

"The Nez Percé (*nay pehr say'*) have come!" cried Sacajawea. All the children raced eagerly to the open space in the center of the village where the councils were held.

The Nez Percé (Pierced Nose) were a friendly tribe who lived over the towering mountains to the sunset. Only a few Shoshoni had ever crossed those mountains. The journey was many suns' hard travel through never-melting snows. It was a "hungry" trail, for there was no food along the way.

There were no buffalo in the Nez Percé country. Each summer Nez Percé braves crossed the mountains to hunt buffalo and trade with the Shoshoni.

The Indians had plenty of time. So they never did anything important without holding a council and going through elaborate ceremonies.

Only warriors sat in a council circle. The women, children, and dogs sat close behind to watch and listen.

First the warriors took off their moccasins as a sign of honesty and friendship. Then Eagle Chief lit his peace pipe. He pointed it east, west, south, and north. He took three slow puffs and passed it to the guests. When all the warriors had smoked there were long flowery speeches.

At last Hoh-hast-ill-pilp, the Nez Percé chief, carefully opened a skin pouch. It was filled with small white shells shaped like the mountain peaks. They glistened in the sun as the snowy peaks did.

The Nez Percé got the shells from Indians who lived near a lake so wide it had no shore and whose water was too bitter to drink.

This Bitter-Shoreless Lake (Pacific Ocean) was many days journey down a great river which flowed from their country toward the sunset.

To the Shoshoni these shells were the most beautiful and sacred of all ornaments. But Eagle Chief pretended not to notice them. Instead he unrolled a bundle of black-tipped, white ermine tails.

Hoh-hast-ill-pilp's eyes gleamed. There were no finer ermine than those the Shoshoni trapped in the mountains. All the Indians prized ermine tails, but Hoh-hast-ill-pilp was especially fond of them.

His best tippet (scarf) was made of ermine tails and the scalp locks, thumbs, and fingers of men he had killed in battle.

Of course he pretended not to be interested in the ermine tails. That was part of the "game." The warriors enjoyed the bargaining. It went on for days. But the women had work to do.

"Come," Flower Woman whispered to Sacajawea. "We must gather service berries."

As Flower Woman stood up, Hoh-hast-ill-pilp saw the wide blue bead belt around her waist. It was made of small blue beads called ti-a-co-mo-shack (chief beads). But he had never seen chief beads that shimmered and shone as these did.

The Indians by the Bitter-Shoreless-Lake valued chief beads more than anything in the world. They would pay many bags of shells for such a belt.

But Flower Woman would not part with the belt. "It belonged to my mother and to her mother before her," she said. "It must be saved for some special purpose. I do not know what that purpose is, but my guardian spirit has said this."

Hoh-hast-ill-pilp said no more. One could not argue with a spirit.

The Shoshoni did not plant gardens. Instead, they gathered wild fruits, vegetables, and roots.

Sacajawea often helped Flower Woman gather berries. When they found more berries than they could eat, they pounded them into a pulp and shaped them into small round cakes. These were dried in the sun and stored in parfleches.

One crisp day in the Moon of Falling Leaves (October) Sacajawea found a bull-berry bush still heavy with fruit. Bullberries are sour until the frost gives them a delicious sweet-sour taste. These were just right.

"You are a fine food gatherer," said Flower Woman when Sacajawea brought the berries home. She put some in a small bowl.

"Take these to Mi-he-wi (Sun Woman)," she said.

Mi-he-wi was an old woman who lived all alone. It was the law of the tribe that every-one must help care for those who had none of their own blanket (family) left. Sacaja-wea had taken Mi-he-wi many gifts.

But now she said, "Why can't I take her dried berry cakes instead? There are only a few bullberries and they are so good."

"They will taste good to Mi-he-wi, too," said Flower Woman. "Is my daughter too selfish to share the good things of life with the poor and helpless?"

Sacajawea had not thought of it that way. She blushed with shame.

"I will take her my share, too," she said. "Then she will have a real feast."

Age had bent Mi-he-wi like a wind-twisted tree on the mountain. Her skin was brown and puckered as a dried apple. But her eyes sparkled with pleasure when she saw the berries.

"You have been kind to an old woman," she said. "I will give you a gift in return."

Sacajawea glanced around the bare tepee in surprise.

Mi-he-wi smiled. "My gift cannot be seen," she said. "My grandmother was a powerful medicine woman — a great healer. She taught me many of her secrets. I will pass them on to you."

Mi-he-wi took Sacajawea into the woods and fields. She taught her to find the magic plants that healed, and how to use them.

There was one to brew for a water that

soothed sore eyes. There were leaves that cured boils and sores, and a root that drew the poison from the bite of a rattlesnake.

Mi-he-wi taught her the secret, magic words that went with gathering the plants and preparing the medicines.

Then winter covered the world with a blanket of snow. They could not go into the fields again, but Mi-he-wi said, "I am content. I have passed the good magic of my grandmother on to one who will guard it well."

CHAPTER 5

The Buffalo Hunt

To the Shoshoni the buffalo were a combination supermarket and department store. They looked forward to the big buffalo hunt in the fall as we look forward to Christmas. It was a time of fun, feasting, and hard work.

If the hunt was successful, they feasted on all the fresh meat they could eat, and dried enough to last through the winter.

"Think how many things our brother, the buffalo, gives us besides food," said Flower Woman one day. She and Sacajawea were pulling and twisting a buffalo hide over a rough log. When they were done it would be soft, cream-colored leather for clothes and sleeping robes. But it was hard work. Talking helped them forget aching backs and arms.

"Almost everything we use is made of leather," she went on. "Buffalo hides are bigger, thicker, and tougher than any others. We use them for tepee covers, clothing, moccasins, ropes, and bridles. What else?"

"Little Bear's new shield," said Sacajawea. She thought proudly of the care with which he had chosen the skin from the neck of an old bull buffalo — the toughest hide of all.

She had not seen him make the shield. That was something each brave went into the forest alone to do. But she knew he must have done everything perfectly. And he must have used exactly the right magic, for now no arrow could pierce his brightly painted shield.

Flower Woman smiled. "That is true. But my daughter should think of the bowls and parfleches made from the same tough hides."

"Shields are so much more exciting." Sacajawea laughed. "Of course I know we use sinews for thread. We make awls (small pointed tools for making holes in leather) from bones. The horns are carved into bows, spoons, and ladles. We boil the hoofs to make glue."

She thought for a moment, then laughed again. "The only thing we can't do much with is the tail."

The Indians believed the buffalo lived in great caves, far to the south, during the winter. In the spring the spirits opened the caves, and the herds thundered out. (Storyteller told of brave Shoshoni warriors who, in a long-ago time, had seen this very thing happen.)

When the spirits thought they had sent enough buffalo to feed and clothe the people for a year, they closed the caves.

But if the spirits were angry, they might send only a few buffalo, or they might not open the caves at all. Then there would be a winter-of-great-hunger.

In the spring the buffalo went north in great herds that covered the plains for miles in all directions. But spring was not the time for the big hunt. Then the buffalo were lean and tough with dull, shaggy coats. After they had grazed on the lush prairie grass all summer, they would be fat and have sleek, shiny coats.

When the first nip of fall was in the air, the Shoshoni prepared for the big hunt. This was a very serious and solemn time, but it was exciting, too.

Scouts rode out in every direction to find the biggest herds and the best place to set up the hunting camp.

The medicine men worked magic and searched for signs and omens.

The hunters stamped and circled around a leaping fire in the sacred dances. (This was to guarantee the killing of much meat without offending the buffalo spirits.)

The chief and the wise men of the council listened carefully to the reports of the scouts. They must think of many things when choosing the place for the hunting camp. There must be a great herd of buffalo nearby. The country must be right for surrounding them. There must be water and plenty of wood

for making fires and building drying racks for the meat.

When the council finally decided where the hunting camp should be, the warriors who acted as police during the hunt took over. Until the end of the hunt, their word would be law. The winter's food supply depended on the success of the hunt. Always, the safety of the tribe must come first.

The year Sacajawea was eight years old the warrior-police rode through camp late one night. "Be ready to move at dawn!" they shouted.

Next morning tepee poles were clattering down before the star people had left the sky. In a few minutes there were only neat bundles of poles and covers where the tepees had been.

The tepee poles were tied together in an upside down V over the shoulders of a pack horse. The ends dragged behind the horse's heels. The tepee cover was lashed to those ends. This was called a travois (*trah voy'*).

Some families moved small things by putting travois on big dogs. But the dogs were not patient and quiet as the pack horses were. They went right on being dogs. They chased squirrels, poked down rabbit holes, upset their loads, and got in everyone's way.

By sun-up the tribe was moving east. The scouts rode far out ahead. Then came warriors, Eagle Chief, and the council. Women, children, and loaded pack animals were next, then the herd boys with the extra horses. Warriors rode at the sides and rear as guards.

It was several days' journey to the spot chosen for the hunting camp. Once there, everyone got to work. The women and children set up the tepees, carried in the sleeping robes and cooking pots, and gathered firewood.

Eagle Chief and the other hunters groomed their best buffalo horses and braided good luck charms into their tails. These horses were carefully trained. They would race beside a running buffalo but swerve instantly if it turned on them. The slightest pressure of the hunter's knees guided his horse so his hands were left free for his weapons. As they worked, the hunters sang the Lucky Hunter's song.

Next morning, in the pale light before dawn, the hunters quietly surrounded the wide valley where a great buffalo herd grazed. They all watched a scout who was posted on the highest hill. When he saw that all the hunters were in their places, he waved his robe in a big circle.

Whooping and yelling, the hunters galloped down the hillsides.

The startled buffalo tried to run. There were hunters in every direction. The buffalo on the edges of the herd tried to get back to the center. In a minute the whole herd was confused. They swirled madly around and around the valley.

The hunters raced in and out of the herd. At such close range almost every arrow killed a buffalo. As soon as one buffalo fell, the hunter raced after another.

At last the buffalo found an opening in the swooping, darting circle of hunters. They went bellowing off between the hills. But, by then, fallen buffalo were scattered all over the valley.

The rest of the tribe had watched the hunt from the hilltops. Now they rushed down the slopes. The hunters slid from their horses. The skinning and butchering began.

There was not a second to waste. The meat must be taken back to camp, cut in thin strips, and hung on drying racks before it could spoil. The hides must be stretched, fastened down with pegs, and scraped while they were still wet and limp.

They each cut choice bits of meat for themselves. But eating did not slow down the butchering. Big chunks of meat were propped over fires to roast. Such tid-bits as liver and tongue they ate raw.

As a buffalo was skinned and cut up, the women packed big bundles of meat and hides onto the horses. Soon a line of women led heavily loaded horses toward the camp. Another line hurried back to the butchering place. When it grew dark, they worked by the light of fires and buffalo-fat torches.

Four times the hunters surrounded big buffalo herds. The drying racks sagged under enough meat to keep hunger from the tepees all winter. The rolling hills near the camp were polka-dotted with hides pegged out to dry.

The hunters could rest. But the rest of the tribe still worked from early morning until late at night, caring for the great stock of supplies. Of course, Sacajawea helped.

"She is the smartest and quickest of all the children," said the old women as they talked among themselves. "She is truly Eagle Chief's daughter."

They all worked as fast as they could. They were uneasy in the open, rolling country. Soon the tepees were taken down again and the travois prepared for the journey back to the mountains.

As they loaded the horses with many hides and great bundles of dried meat, the Shoshoni said to each other, "Truly, this will be a long-remembered winter-of-enough-food."

And each one thanked the Great Spirit.

CHAPTER 6

Sacajawea's Sacrifice

Two years later everything was different. Since early spring there had been no rain. Day after day the blazing sun burned the grass and dried the streams. Forest fires raged in the mountains.

The Thunder Moon (August) came and went. Still the scouts did not find a buffalo herd.

"Surely the spirits are angry with us," the Shoshoni whispered to one another.

At last Eagle Chief summoned the tribe to a council.

"My people," he said, "even through the-time-of-much food (summer) we have been hungry. Many of our possessions were burned. To live through the winter we must kill many buffalo.

"But this year the buffalo have taken strange paths. To find them we must go far into the country of our enemies." He looked slowly around the circle of grim-faced warriors.

"It is better to die fighting than to die of cold and hunger," he said.

No one spoke. That meant they all agreed.

Eagle Chief raised his right hand high. "We will start for the buffalo plains at dawn," he said.

Little Bear rode with the hunters now. He looked so tall and straight and brave on his spirited, red- and white-spotted buffalo pony that Sacajawea's heart thumped with pride. Already he had won many feathers (honors). She was sure he would be a great chief some day.

Sometimes he let her ride beside him. "What landmarks have we passed?" he asked.

"A great red rock shaped like a beaver's head," said Sacajawea. "And canyons so deep and narrow we could hardly see the rushing river far below . . ."

Little Bear smiled. "You have remembered well."

Sacajawea was sure there was not, in all the world, another brother so kind to a little sister who had seen only ten snows.

At last the scouts found a small herd of buffalo.

"It is near the place where three rivers join to form the one the Sioux (*soo*) call the Mini Sose (Muddy Water)," they said. "Wood and water for the hunting camp can be found where the rivers meet."

Many of the women were afraid. "The valley is wide," they said. "There are no forests, only bushes and small trees. There is no hiding place for those who cannot run fast. They will all be killed if our enemies come."

"When I was gathering berries, I found a cave near the river," said Sacajawea. "The opening is covered by piles of brush. It would be a good hiding place."

The old and feeble, the small children and the babies were hidden in the cave while the others worked. But still the people were worried and fearful. There was no laughter in camp. The only songs were prayer-songs to the spirits.

One morning Flower Woman clasped her blue bead belt around Sacajawea's waist.

"You are old enough to wear this now," she said. "Guard it carefully until it is time for you to pass it on."

"How will I know when that time comes?" asked Sacajawea.

"I cannot tell you," said Flower Woman. "Long ago I had a dream. In my dream a trumpeter swan flew with many eagles. But I do not know what it meant."

A short time later, crashing, roaring, thunder-like noises came from the direction in which the hunters had gone. The people looked at one another in fright. What *could* it be?

"It is the magic smoke-sticks!" cried an old warrior. "Enemies have attacked our hunters. Soon they will find our camp. Run! Run for your lives!"

Even as he spoke, yelling, hideously painted warriors galloped over a rise and swept down on the camp.

Sacajawea was near the river. There was a thick tangle of berry bushes beside her. She threw herself onto the ground and wriggled behind them. She wedged herself far back in a crack in the riverbank.

All through the long, terrible day she lay without moving.

Once enemy warriors rode close but their horses shied away from the thorny bushes. They rode on without seeing Sacajawea or the nearby entrance to the cave.

At last she heard the hoofbeats of many horses leaving camp. Still she made herself lie quietly.

"Some of the enemy may have waited to see if any Shoshoni were hidden," she thought.

She was right.

Long purple shadows were creeping across the land when there was a cry from one of the babies in the cave. Instantly it was stopped. But that had been long enough. An enemy had heard. There was a sudden pounding of hoofs as he raced toward the sound.

"Now he will find the helpless ones," thought Sacajawea. "I must save them. There is no one else."

She thought quickly. If the enemy saw her he would think that she had made the sound. But she must lead him away from the cave . . .

A daring plan flashed into her mind. There was a sandbar a little way down the river. If she were swift enough she might run to it, cross the river, and climb the high bank on the other side.

Did she have the courage? She *must* have. It was the *only* way. She forced down her fear. The warrior had almost reached the cave.

"Guardian spirit, lend my feet your wings," she whispered.

She darted from her hiding place. For a moment the startled warrior stared. Then,

with a terrifying whoop, he quirted his horse after her.

Sacajawea's feet hardly seemed to touch the earth as she raced along the shore. But when she plunged into the shallow water over the sandbar the swift current dragged at her. When she reached the middle of the river there was a great splashing close behind her. She felt the horse's hot breath . . .

Sacajawea knew she had lost the race. She bowed her head for the death blow she expected. To her amazement the enemy warrior reached down and pulled her up on his horse. Then he wheeled his horse about and galloped off after his tribesmen.

He was a Hidatsa warrior. The Hidatsa lived in permanent villages far to the east. They raised gardens. Gardening was hard work. It was for women and children — not braves. The warriors raided other tribes and brought back strong boys and girls for slaves.

Sacajawea did not know this. She had never heard of corn, squash, or any garden vegetable. She did not know it was possible for people to grow the food they needed.

The next morning the Hidatsa started the long journey home. They had captured four boys, several girls, and many fine Shoshoni horses.

Sacajawea saw Eagle Chief's fiery, black stallion, and Little Bear's spotted pony, among them. Then she no longer hoped that her father and brother still lived.

She would not let her sorrow show in her face. She rode straight and tall as Eagle Chief's daughter should. She kept back the tears by forcing herself to memorize every detail of this strange, wide country.

Each day the shining snow-capped mountains grew smaller in the distance behind them. At last they were gone.

"Some day I *will* see them again," Sacajawea vowed secretly.

The Hidatsa village was on a bluff, high above the Missouri River. The lodges were like great, upside-down bowls covered with earth. Grass grew over them. Thin plumes of smoke curled up from smokeholes in the top.

Running Wolf, the warrior who had captured Sacajawea, led her to his lodge. They went through a short, tunnel-like passage into a large, round room. A circle of tall posts held up the roof. Between the posts were the skin beds. Food, clothing, and garden tools were stored between the beds and the wall.

Sacajawea couldn't help staring. Tribes that moved often could not have many possessions. To her those things were great wealth.

The fire was in a hole in the center of the room. Running Wolf motioned toward a woman cooking meat over the hot coals.

He spoke to Sacajawea in sign language. "Grass Woman, my wife, will tell you what to do. If you do not work I will beat you. If you try to run away I will kill you. Do you understand?"

Sacajawea nodded. She knew he meant what he said.

Running Wolf and Grass Woman were not unkind when they saw that Sacajawea worked hard and willingly. But for a long time the Shoshoni children were closely watched. They had no chance to talk together.

One day, when Sacajawea was thirteen, she was working near Red Plume, another Shoshoni.

"Sacajawea," she said in a low voice. "My brother and I plan to escape the first night of the dead moon (the three nights when the moon cannot be seen). Will you come too?"

For a moment Sacajawea was so homesick she thought she could not bear it. But she said slowly, "I will stay here."

"Are you afraid?" demanded Red Plume,

who often let words fly from her mouth too soon. "Or have you forgotten you are a Shoshoni?"

Sacajawea's eyes flashed. "It is because I remember the suffering of our tribe that I will not go. There are none of my own blanket left. The tribe would be forced to care for me. I would only be a burden.

"I will come when I am older and can care for myself."

"How could a girl make such a journey alone?" said Red Plume. "If you do not come now, you will never see the Shoshoni or the Shining Mountains again."

Before Sacajawea could answer she heard a clear flute-like call. She looked up. A long single line of birds flew toward the Shining Mountains.

"I do not know how it will be," she said, "but some day I *will* come. I promise."

Even as she spoke, things were happening in the faraway city of Washington, D.C., which would someday help her keep that promise.

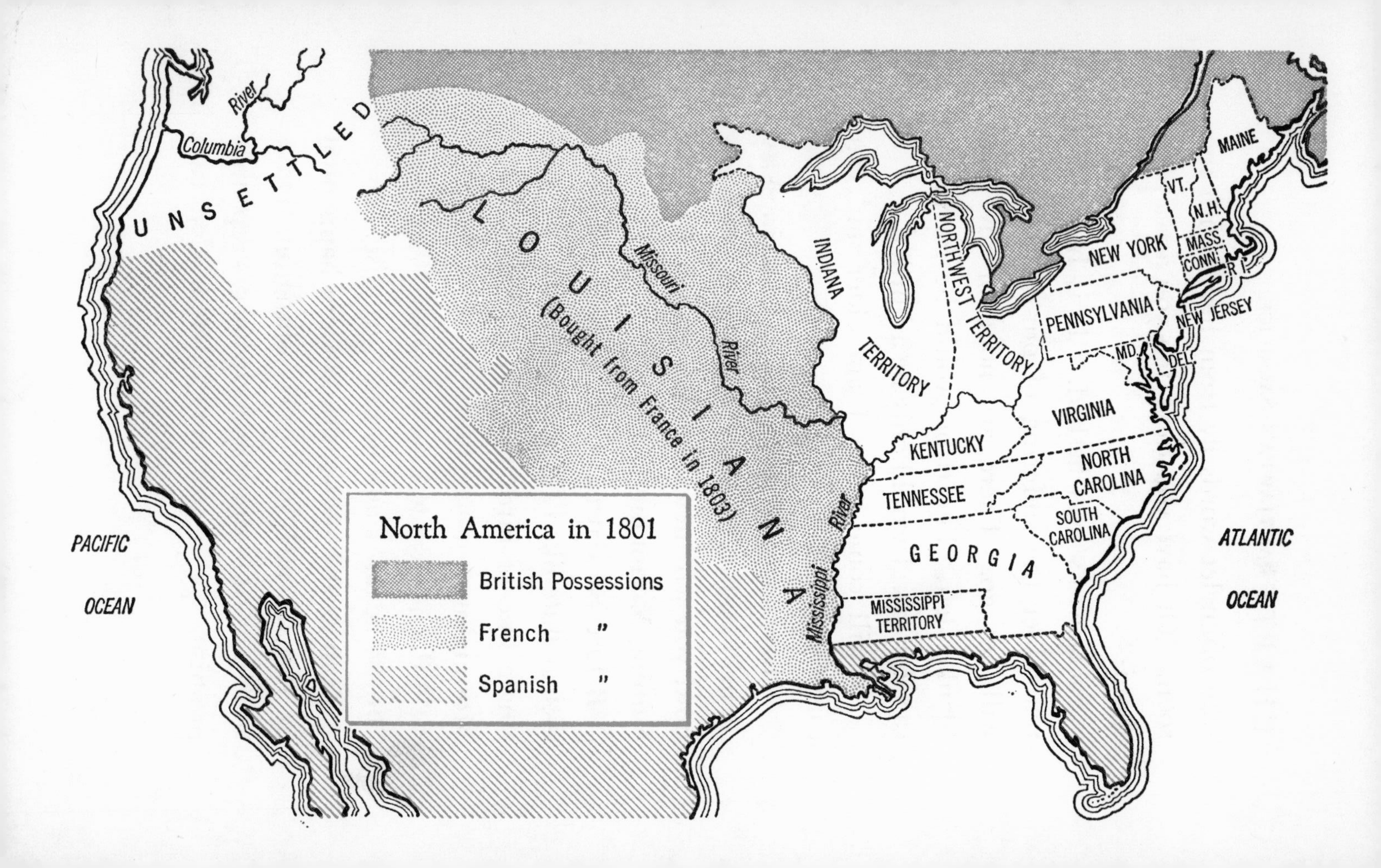
North America in 1801
British Possessions
French "
Spanish "
UNSETTLED
Columbia
River
LOUISIANA
(Bought from France in 1803)
Missouri
River
Mississippi
River
INDIANA
TERRITORY
NORTHWEST TERRITORY
KENTUCKY
TENNESSEE
MISSISSIPPI
TERRITORY
GEORGIA
SOUTH
CAROLINA
NORTH
CAROLINA
VIRGINIA
MD.
DEL.
PENNSYLVANIA
NEW JERSEY
NEW YORK
VT.
N.H.
MASS.
CONN.
R.I.
MAINE
PACIFIC
OCEAN
ATLANTIC
OCEAN

CHAPTER 7

The Quest of Lewis and Clark

It was March 4, 1801. Thomas Jefferson was being inaugurated as the third President of the United States.

He was a man who looked far into the future. He believed the new little United States must have plenty of room to grow. But England, France, and Spain already owned most of the land in North America. The United States must act quickly or it would be squeezed into a small strip along the eastern seaboard forever.

France owned a great tract of land, west of the Mississippi River, called Louisiana. The United States bought it for $15,000,000. Most of it was still unexplored. Jefferson asked Congress to send an expedition to explore the unknown wilderness beyond the Mississippi.

There were other, secret reasons for the expedition which only a trusted few could know.

Many people still believed in the old dream of a short trade route to the Orient. They were sure there must be a way to cross North America by water. If this route could be found, American ships would not have to make the long voyage around Cape Horn.

But there was still another reason — the most important of all. In 1792, Captain Robert Gray had sailed up the Pacific Coast and into a great river which he named the Columbia, after his staunch ship.

According to the laws of nations, that gave the United States claim to the whole Columbia River basin. But the British did not want the United States to have any land on the Pacific Coast. They, too, claimed the Columbia. They said no American ship had entered the river.

If Americans could find the source of the Columbia, and travel down the river to the Pacific Ocean before the British did, the Columbia River basin would belong to the United States.

The British were already searching for the source of the Columbia. There was not a moment to be lost.

Many geographers thought the eastward flowing Missouri River, and the westward flowing Columbia, started at almost the same spot. So the expedition would travel up the Missouri to find the source of the Columbia. This might even be the short way to the Orient they were searching for.

The leader of such an expedition could not be an ordinary man. He must be trustworthy and loyal; brave, but not reckless; quick-thinking, but cool-headed. He must be firm and determined, but still patient and kind. He must be well educated to take care of scientific matters. But he must also know how to live in the wilderness.

President Jefferson knew exactly the right

man. When Meriwether Lewis was a boy, he had lived near the President's home in Virginia. Even then he had dreamed of exploring the wilderness beyond the Mississippi. When he grew up, he joined the army and rose to Captain. When Mr. Jefferson became President, he appointed him his secretary. They spent many hours planning the expedition together.

They agreed that such a dangerous venture must have two leaders. If something happened to one, the other could carry on.

Lewis chose red-headed William Clark. They had been boyhood friends. Later they had served in the same army company.

They were a tall, handsome pair, gallant officers and gentlemen. Both were brilliant men and fine leaders, expert marksmen and horsemen. Both had spent much time in the wilderness.

They were different in many ways, but they worked together perfectly. Never, in all their lives, did they have the slightest misunderstanding.

They were a tall, handsome pair.

Lewis was quiet, a dreamer and planner — with the iron will to carry his plans through. Once he dreamed of a goal he never stopped until he reached it.

He loved fine clothes. His ruffled and gold-braided dress uniforms, and his plumed cocked hats, were his greatest pride. His black hair was cut in the latest style.

He was the scientific specialist. He also planned and bought the supplies.

Lively, broad-shouldered Clark wore his hair in an old-fashioned style. He had merry blue eyes and a kind heart. He was full of energy and bounce. He laughed and joked and said what he thought — firmly. He liked Indians and knew how to deal with them.

Clark was such a fine geographer it sometimes seemed that he must have a compass built inside his head.

Many members of Congress believed the expedition a foolish waste of money. "What do we want with a wilderness beyond the Mississippi?" they grumbled. At last they grudgingly gave them $2,500 for all expenses.

Captain Lewis had to be a careful shopper to stretch the money to cover everything they needed. He bought sugar, tea, flour, corn-meal, bacon, salt-pork, salt and pepper, and portable (dried) soup.

He bought tools, weapons, and scientific instruments.

The Indians did not use money. They traded goods. For trading, and gifts to the Indians, he bought beads, paint, mirrors, tinkling bells, and ribbons. He bought needles, red cloth, brass kettles, and flags. As special gifts for chiefs he bought bronze "peace" medals. These had President Jefferson's head on one side. On the other side were two hands clasped above a peace pipe.

They could not afford to take a doctor, so he bought simple medicines.

Finally he bought a bateau (*bah toh':* river barge) which took twenty-two men to row. With its big square sail it looked like the Vikings' "dragon boats."

The party arrived at the mouth of the Missouri in December. They could not travel

up the river until spring. They built a winter camp across the river from St. Louis. There the men drilled, hunted, and built two pirogues (*pih rohgs':* big, flat-bottomed row-boats with sails). One was painted white and one red.

Trappers and traders often stopped at the camp. None of them had been very far up the Missouri, but they all told tall tales of what was in the wilderness.

"There's a whole range of rock salt mountains," said one. "The Shining Mountains, the Indians call them."

"Salt, nothin'," said another. "Those mountains are pure crystal. When the sun hits them they glitter and glare enough to blind a man."

"Indians ten feet tall live in them," said another. "Cannibals, most likely. The other Indians keep their distance from those Shining Mountains. Yes, siree!"

They all agreed that there was a volcano somewhere in the wilderness, and monsters so tall that they bent down to eat the tree tops, and that they had scales instead of fur.

No one knew what the truth really was. The expedition was going to find out.

The Captains had picked their men carefully. They were all members of the United States Army while they were with the expedition. Some, like Sergeants Ordway and Pryor, were army regulars who had volunteered for this duty.

Some, like John Colter and the Fields brothers, Joseph and Reuben, were frontiersmen.

Drewyer was a hunter, scout, and interpreter. He knew the speech of many Indian tribes and the Indian sign language which all the Plains tribes understood.

Cruzatte was a French voyageur (*vwah yah zhur′*: riverman). His one good eye read the meaning of every ripple in the water. Around the campfires he coaxed rollicking, toe-teasing tunes from his home made fiddle.

York, Clark's Negro servant, was as cheerful and lively as Clark. He was a huge man with mighty muscles. But he was light as thistledown when he danced to Cruzatte's fiddle, as he loved to do.

Scannon, Lewis's huge Newfoundland dog, was the mascot.

On May 14, 1804, the expedition started up the Missouri. The pirogues went first. Then came the bateau. Her white sail puffed out in the prairie wind. The American flag, proudly flaunting its seventeen stars, flew from the mast.

Cruzatte started a lively song. The men sang loud and strong. Their flashing oars kept time. Adventure was just ahead . . .

Throughout the spring, and the choking hot prairie summer, the men rowed, pushed, and pulled their boats up the twisting river. They grew lean and tough-muscled and as brown as the muddy Missouri. They learned to think and act as a team.

President Jefferson had asked the Captains to keep a careful record of their journey. They wrote in their journals every day. They told what had happened. They described the country and everything that was new and

strange to them. Neither was good at spelling, but Clark used the most imagination. He often spelled a word six different ways without once finding the right one.

They stopped several times to hold councils with the Indians. It was part of their job to make friends with the tribes they met and tell them the United States now owned the land.

The war-like Sioux tried to scare them, but they soon found these men could not be bluffed. The Captains warned them sternly that the Great Father in Washington wished his red children to live in peace together.

As they went on, the days grew shorter. V-shaped flocks of birds flew south. At night ice formed on still water. Short snowstorms whirled from gray clouds. It was time to think of a winter camp.

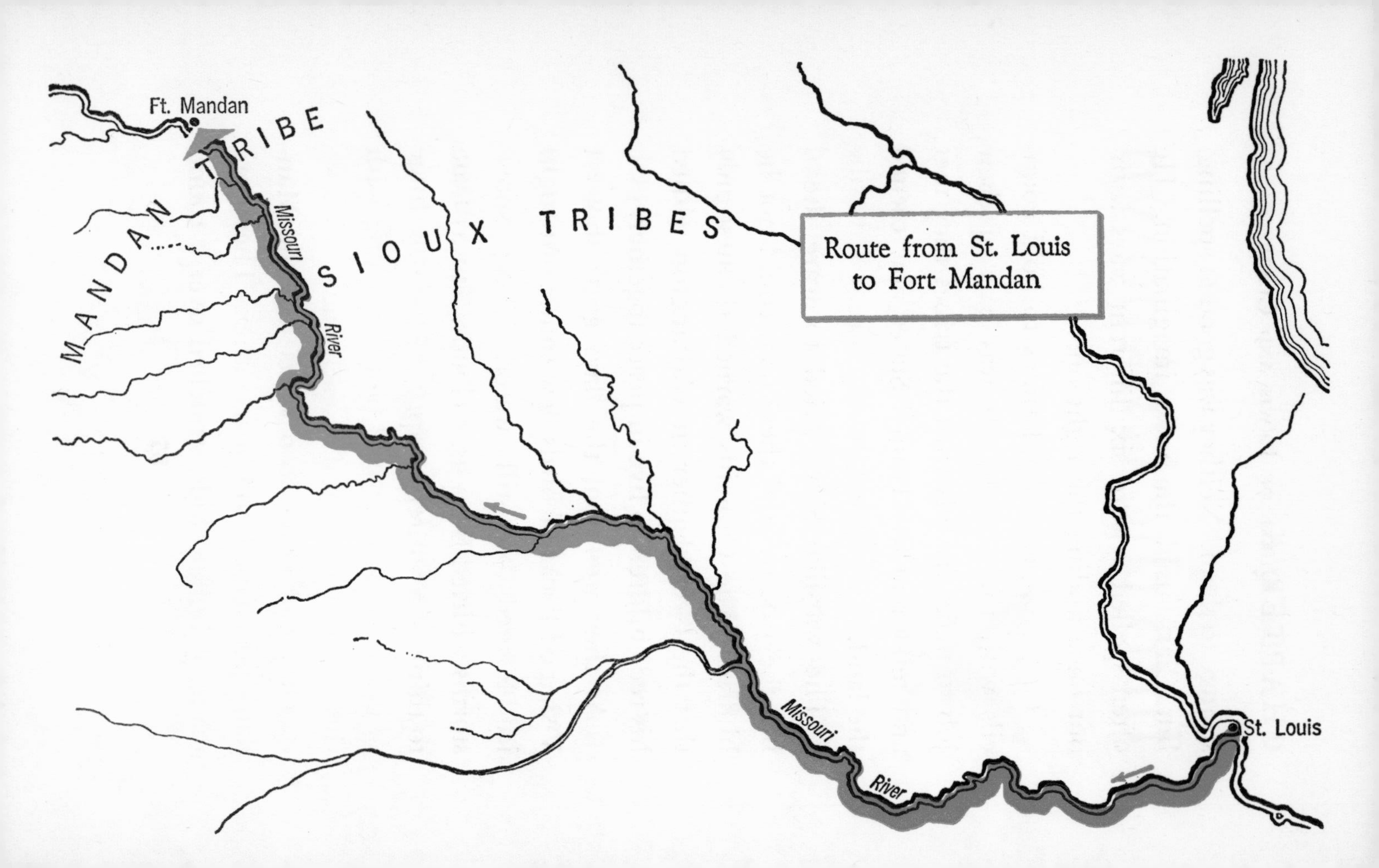
Route from St. Louis
to Fort Mandan
Ft. Mandan
MANDAN TRIBE
SIOUX TRIBES
Missouri River
Missouri River
St. Louis

CHAPTER 8

Into the Unknown

Late in October they reached the country of the Mandans, a peaceful tribe who made war only on those who attacked them.

The Mandans had heard of the white men coming up the river in their great white-winged canoes. When the boats stopped, Black Cat, the grand chief, came to greet them. He invited the Captains to dinner in his own lodge.

The others strolled through the village. They had never seen anything like the huge Mandan lodges. Several families, along with their best horses, lived in each one.

They had never seen boats like the Mandan's pot-shaped bull boats either. They were made of buffalo hide stretched over a round willow frame. They were so light a squaw could carry one on her head.

The Mandans were just as curious about the strangers. They stared at York in open-mouthed wonder. Here was a mighty man whose skin was not red, not white, but still a different color. This could not be! He must be painted!

Fun-loving York grinned and let them rub his skin to see if the color would come off.

"Tell them I'm a wild monster Captain Clark tamed," he said to Drewyer. With an earth-shaking roar he grabbed Cruzatte and pretended he was going to eat him.

Such chills and thrills! Such shouts and yells! Such an uproar! The Captains rushed out to see what was going on.

York dropped Cruzatte. They tried to look as innocent as the babies in their cradle-boards.

"Don't be *quite* so ferocious," said Clark, trying not to laugh. "You might really frighten our friends, the Mandans. Why not dance for them, instead?"

Cruzatte struck up a lively tune and the men danced. The Mandans had never heard such merry music nor seen such dancing. The men had never had such a delighted audience. They did Irish jigs and Scottish reels. They leaped into the air and cracked their heels. York did a cakewalk, and a buck and wing. He danced as if he had no bones. The Mandans yelled and shouted with joy. When Scannon took a few lumbering steps after York, the crowd went wild.

Never had there been such a party! The moon was high in the sky and everyone was in a very good humor when it was finally over.

The Captains decided to build the winter camp about three miles down the river from the Mandan village.

Early and late the woods rang with the sound of axes biting into big cottonwood trees. Ice-edged winds were bringing snow and sleet. The men were eager to get inside.

On November 20, Fort Mandan was finished. It was built in the shape of a hollow triangle. There were eight cabins inside a stockade of tall, sharply pointed logs. At one corner was a tower where sentries stood guard day and night. The Captains were taking no chances on surprise raids by the surly Sioux.

Blizzards howled out of the north. The temperature dropped to 45 degrees below zero.

Inside the fort it was snug and warm. Everyone was busy. Hunting parties went after meat. What they did not eat was smoked. The hides were tanned and made into moccasins, shirts, and leggings. They repaired tools and weapons. Everything must be ready for spring when they started up the river again.

Indians came to the fort every day. They told the Captains many things about that part of the country and the tribes who lived there. The Captains wrote it all down in their journals.

All the Indians said the Missouri began in the Shining Mountains far to the west.

Here was a problem. Boats could not

climb mountains. The expedition must have horses to carry the supplies over the mountains, and guides for the unknown mountain passes.

"The Shoshoni, who live deep in the Shining Mountains, have great herds of fine horses," said a brave.

"You cannot find them to buy horses," a chief warned. "They are part spirit. They leap from crag to crag. They vanish into solid rock."

"They are fierce warriors," said another. "Braves rash enough to enter their mountains do not return. Only when hunger drives the Shoshoni to the Plains do other tribes see them."

The Captains did not believe in evil spirits. But how could they get horses and guides from a tribe they could not find?

One day Touissant Charbonneau (*shar bon oh'*), a French Canadian trapper and trader who lived nearby, came to the fort. He asked for a job as guide and interpreter.

"I have been farther up the Missouri than

any other white man," he said proudly.

"Have you been to the country of the Shoshoni?" asked Lewis.

"No," said Charbonneau. "But my wife is a Shoshoni. She was captured by the Hidatsa as a child. I bought her from them."

The Captains looked at each other. Could a woman stand such a trip?

Charbonneau saw the look. "Sacajawea is young and strong," he said. "She is only sixteen. She is not an ordinary squaw. The Shoshoni are a proud, noble people, and she is the daughter of a great chief."

Sacajawea and Charbonneau came to Fort Mandan to live. Her face showed nothing when the Captains questioned her. But she wondered why these white men with many guns *really* wanted to find the Shoshoni. She would watch and listen carefully. Long before they reached the Shining Mountains she would know whether they spoke the truth.

"I am still a Shoshoni — Eagle Chief's daughter," she thought. "If they are lying, they will all die in the mountains. I will die with them before I will betray my people."

One morning Sacajawea heard the men laughing and shouting, "Merry Christmas! Merry Christmas!"

She watched with wide black eyes as they celebrated their Great Good Medicine Day.

The men gave each other home made Christmas gifts, and tobacco and handkerchiefs they had carefully saved. Dinner was a feast of all the best food in the fort.

In the afternoon they held a "Christmas Ball" around a roaring fire in the courtyard. "Gentlemen" in worn buckskins bowed to bearded "Ladies." The "ladies" curtsied and pointed the toes of their heavy boots. They all stepped high and fancy as they promenaded and sashayed.

That night the men sang carols around the cabin hearths. Outside the wind howled and the northern lights danced their ghost dance in the sky. But inside the little cabins the spirit of Christmas was warm and bright.

Day after day Sacajawea sat quietly in a

corner of the Captain's office. Soon she could understand many English words, but she did not let on. She watched and listened carefully. The Captains spoke the same words to all the Indians who came to the fort.

"You are all children of the Great White Father now," they said. "You must live in peace together."

"Those were the words of Storyteller," thought Sacajawea.

But the words meant little. She watched their actions, too.

When they settled quarrels among the tribes, they were stern but just. They treated the sick with their own medicines. When the hunters brought back meat, they shared it with the Indians. They paid the Indians for anything they wanted. *Always,* they kept their word.

"Still," thought Sacajawea, "other white men gave these tribes guns. The Shoshoni have none. Perhaps these men would not treat the Shoshoni as they treat the tribes along the river."

They were all so kind and friendly that Sacajawea found it hard *not* to like them. Scannon, who was big as a colt, put his head in her lap and wagged his tail blissfully when she rubbed his ears.

Sacajawea sighed. It was very hard to know what was right. She must watch carefully for signs from the spirits.

"Sacajawea is too hard to spell," said Clark as he wrote in his journal one day. "I'm going to call you 'Janey.' "

When Sacajawea's son, Baptiste, was born February 11, 1805, Clark said, "That's too hard to spell, too. I'll call him 'Pompey' after the Indian word for first-born."

At last the snow melted on the prairies. The ice on the river cracked and roared as it broke up and swirled downstream.

The men hollowed out six logs for dugout canoes. The river would soon be too shallow for the bateau. They loaded it with things they were sending back to President Jefferson. There were Indian clothes, pots, painted robes, animal skins and skeletons, stuffed

birds and snakes, and mice and insects. There was a burrowing squirrel, a prairie hen, and four magpies all alive — and very lively.

On April 7, the bateau started down the river to St. Louis, 1,600 miles away. The rest of the party waved good-by and started up the Missouri on their way to the Pacific Ocean.

The white pirogue was the flagship now. She carried the Captains, all their scientific instruments, important papers, and medicines. Sacajawea and Pompey were aboard her, too, and Scannon, who barked happily at everything they passed.

A week later Charbonneau said, "Beyond this spot no white man has ever been."

The men cheered. Oars and paddles dipped and flashed. The Stars and Stripes flew proudly from the masthead of the white pirogue.

Now the expedition was truly exploring the unknown.

CHAPTER 9

Danger on the Missouri

Now the rivers, lakes, canyons, mountains, and even some of the animals they passed had no names. The Captains had to call them something in their journals and on maps. They named hundreds of things as they went along. They named something for every member of the party. They named things for pretty girls back home.

Clark meant to name a river for pert Judy Hancock, back in Virginia, but he absent-mindedly wrote "Judith" instead. The Judith it is to this day.

"Eagles are thick as robins along these river bluffs," said Lewis one day.

"They are fierce, noble looking birds,"

said Clark. "There could not be a better symbol for the United States." He took a ten dollar gold piece from his pocket. Everyone crowded around to compare the eagle on the coin with the real birds.

As she looked at it Sacajawea's eyes sparkled with joy. "Eagles are Shoshoni," she thought. "If eagles are the guardian spirits of the Americans, the Captains speak the truth. We are of the same tribe. It is right for me to lead the Americans to the Shoshoni. It is the sign from the spirits for which I have waited."

Great herds of buffalo, elk, deer, and antelope grazed on the green prairie. But there was one animal the men had not yet seen — a grizzly bear. They often talked about grizzlies as they sat around the campfire.

"The Indians say they stand eight or ten feet tall, when they rear up on their hind feet," said Joe Fields.

"And weigh five or six hundred pounds," added Colter.

They all laughed. Everyone had a tall tale

of what *he* would do if he met a grizzly.

Sacajawea tried to tell them how savage the bears were.

"To kill one is the bravest deed a warrior can do," she said. "Some tribes count it the same as killing *two* armed warriors."

The men still laughed, but a few days later they stopped.

Six of the best hunters saw a grizzly near the river. They spread out and crept up on him silently. When they were about forty feet away, Drewyer, Colter, and two others fired. All four shots hit the bear.

Instead of tumbling over in a heap he reared up. With a bellowing roar, he spread pitchfork-like claws and charged Drewyer and Colter.

All the boasts of twisting a grizzly's tail were forgotten. They raced for the river. The bear galloped after them, gaining with every leap.

The Fields brothers fired. Both balls hit the bear. One broke his shoulder. It only slowed him for a second. That was long

enough for Drewyer and Colter to jump into a canoe and shove off.

Whirling around, the bear charged after the Fields. There was no time to reload. Dropping their guns, they leaped from a twenty-foot bluff into the river. The furious bear hurled himself after them.

The Fields swam for their lives. The bear was a better swimmer. They could hear his snarling, snuffling breath coming closer — fast. Every second they expected to feel his snapping teeth.

Drewyer took careful aim and shot again. The bullet pierced an angry red eye and went straight to the grizzly's brain. Slowly he sank to the river bottom.

The men waited a long time to be sure he was really dead. When they dragged the huge carcass ashore, there were eight rifle balls in him. He measured almost nine feet from head to foot.

"We'd better take him back to camp," said Joe Fields, who was still green and shaky, "or they will never believe us."

But the rest of the party were having troubles of their own.

The Captains were walking along the shore. They were in high spirits. It was May 14. Just a year ago they had left St. Louis. Now they were 2,200 miles up the winding Missouri.

They did not see the storm clouds sweeping across the sky until suddenly the sun was blotted out. A raging wind whipped the river into towering waves. It caught the sail of the white pirogue and flipped it on its side like a toy.

The Captains raced for the shore. They fired their guns to attract attention and shouted orders. No one heard.

Several of the men aboard could not swim. They were too frightened to move. To the frantic Captains it seemed hours before Cruzatte managed to cut the sail free. The white pirogue slowly righted, but it was almost filled with water. Much of the cargo was floating about the boat. Some was tossing in the river.

Lewis threw down his gun and tore off his coat. Clark grabbed him.

"You'll drown in that wild, icy water!" he said. "Those waves are like cliffs."

"I would rather die than lose our instruments, papers, and medicines," cried Lewis.

"Look!" said Clark, pointing. Sacajawea, with Pompey on her back, was calmly swimming about rescuing the things that had been washed overboard. As they watched, she

swam back to the boat and gathered up the articles floating near there.

Cruzatte set two men to bailing, and the others rowed. By the time the white pirogue reached shore the storm was over. Hastily they spread the cargo in the sun to dry.

To the Captains' great joy only a few small items had been lost.

"Without Sacajawea's courage and quick thinking, we would have lost our most valuable possessions," said Lewis. "We could not have gone on. The expedition would have failed."

Late in May they saw a mighty range of mountains far ahead. Their snowy peaks glittered and sparkled in the sun.

"At last," said Clark, "I understand why the Indians call them the 'Shining Mountains.' "

They came to a place where the river divided into two streams of almost equal size.

The Captains were so sure the south fork was the Missouri that Lewis named the north fork the Marias. But they must *know.* They could not waste time traveling up the wrong river if they were to cross the Rockies before winter.

The Indians had told them of a great falls on the Missouri. Lewis decided to take four men and go overland along the south fork. If they found the falls, he would send back word for the others to follow.

Three days later they heard a far-off steady roar. A column of mist rose in the air like smoke. Then they saw a wide, shining sheet of water plunging over a ledge eighty feet high. Now they were sure — the south fork *was* the Missouri.

Soon the river would be too shallow for the pirogues. So, while they waited, Clark and the others hid the red pirogue on an island. Then they made a cache (hiding place in the earth) for all the supplies they could spare.

For once the men did not laugh and joke as they worked. Sacajawea was sick. Always she had marched staunchly along beside them with little Pompey on her back. Now she lay pale and still on the white pirogue.

Clark tried all their medicines. Finally he bled her. That was a remedy doctors of that time used when they did not know what else to do. But Sacajawea grew worse.

The men talked in low tones of all the things she had done to make their life easier.

"Remember, when the rattlesnake bit me, how she tramped away off in the hills and found a root that took out all the poison," said Joe Fields.

"And how often she gathered wild plants and berries for our meals," said Reuben.

Everyone had something to add to the story of Sacajawea's help and thoughtfulness.

"I guess we just took it all for granted," said Colter sadly.

Now they brought their softest antelope skins for her bed. They picked clumsy bouquets of wildflowers for her and took turns caring for Pompey.

Clark was the best "baby sitter." Often he strode along, shouting orders, and giving the men a hand, with the tiny black-haired baby tucked under one arm.

As they traveled up the river to where Lewis waited, they passed a mineral spring.

"The water smells so bad it *must* be good for the health," said Clark. He gave Sacajawea large doses.

No one knew what finally helped, but she began to get better. Soon she was able to eat a little of the rich buffalo soup they made for her. The first day she took a few wobbly steps Cruzatte brought out his fiddle. The men sang and danced around the campfire. Sacajawea was going to get well!

CHAPTER 10

The Land of the Shoshoni

They had to carry their boats around the falls. They hid the white pirogue and made another cache. Now that everything must be carried it was astonishing how much they could do without.

They cut down trees and built two crude carts to haul the heavy canoes. The wheels were round slices sawed from a tree trunk.

The Indians did not use wheels, so Sacajawea had never seen one before. She thought they were a wonderful invention of the Captains. The men harnessed themselves to the heavy carts and dragged them along under the blazing sun. Clouds of gnats and mosquitoes settled on their bare, sweating skin. When they stopped to rest, the exhausted men dropped to the ground and instantly fell asleep.

Cactus covered the ground. Sacajawea had taught them to make double-soled moccasins of rawhide. But the lance-like thorns pierced rawhide like paper. Every step left a bloody mark. Scannon licked his sore paws and limped along with the men.

"No one complains. They all go on cheerfully," the Captains proudly agreed.

Sometimes there were cloudbursts with hailstones so big they knocked men down. One day Clark, Charbonneau, Sacajawea, and Pompey were caught in a cloudburst.

They took shelter underneath a rock ledge in a deep gully. Hailstones banged against the ledge. It seemed as if all the water in the sky were falling at once. But they were dry and snug. Sacajawea took Pompey from his cradleboard. He stretched and kicked happily.

Suddenly there was a strange, grinding roar. A great wall of water was rushing down the gully, sweeping rocks and trees before it.

Charbonneau was so frightened he fairly flew up the steep sides of the gully. Clark stopped to grab his gun and shot pouch.

Sacajawea snatched up Pompey and tried to climb. But she could not keep a firm grasp on the slippery rocks with the baby in one arm. She kept sliding back. The fast rising water lapped at her moccasins. Charbonneau tried to haul her up by her arm.

That only threw her off balance. Clark got behind her. With one hand he pushed her up ahead of him. The water rose to his waist as they struggled up. By the time they scrambled over the top of the gully the water behind them was fifteen feet deep.

"Captain Clark saved my life — and Pompey's," Sacajawea told the men later.

At last the trip around the falls was over. They paddled up the Missouri again. It became a swift, narrow channel as the towering mountains closed in.

The Captains were worried. Soon they must have horses. They had seen signs of Indians, but no Indians. Could they find the Shoshoni?

"Perhaps they have seen us and think we are enemies," said Lewis. He ordered that each canoe fly an American flag to show they were friends.

When they came to the place where the three rivers meet to form the Missouri, they called it the Three Forks. They did not know which river was the true Missouri.

They named one for President Jefferson, one for James Madison, Secretary of State, and one for Albert Gallatin, Secretary of the Treasury.

"This is where my people were camped when the Hidatsa came," said Sacajawea. Then she pointed to the northern fork, which they had named the Jefferson.

"This river flows from the land of the Shoshoni."

They started up the Jefferson. Soon it became a rushing, tumbling mountain stream. Often it cut between rock walls that rose straight from the water. Paddles were useless against the swift current. The men tied tow ropes around their waists and dragged the heavy canoes through icy water up to their armpits. Sharp rocks tore their moccasins and cut their feet. Rattlesnakes coiled on every rocky ledge.

Early one morning Colter leaped from his blanket with a wild yell. The startled men grabbed for their guns.

"A rattler! It was curled up in my blanket with me!" yelled Colter from the middle of the river.

"Ah, he just wanted to be friendly," said Drewyer.

The men whooped and laughed.

"They are in good spirits in spite of their suffering," the Captains agreed.

One day Sacajawea pointed eagerly to a great red-colored rock. Her eyes sparkled.

"Beaver's Head," she said. "It is near the place where this river begins.

"From that place we must go across a mountain," she went on. "There, by a river that flows toward the sunset, live the Shoshoni."

The Captains talked it over. They could not cross the mountains without horses to carry their baggage. They must get them soon. It was only August, but that morning the ink had been frozen in a quill pen.

"If winter storms trap us in these endless peaks, our bones will be here in the spring," said Lewis grimly.

He decided to take three men and go ahead to find the Shoshoni. The others would take the canoes as far up the Jefferson as they could, then wait for his return.

Sacajawea taught him the Shoshoni signal of friendship. "Spread your blanket wide, wave it high over your head, then bring it to earth. Do this three times," she said.

"Paint the faces of any Shoshoni you meet with red paint," she went on. "That is the sign of peace."

She had them say "Ta-ba-bone," the Shoshoni word for "white man" over and over.

The two Captains shook hands gravely.

"I will find the Shoshoni and bring back horses," said Lewis, "or I will not come back at all."

Lewis and his men carried light packs and traveled fast. Two days later they came to a place where the river divided. Neither stream was big enough to float the canoes. Lewis wrote a note telling Clark to wait there and left it on a pole.

They followed the stream which Sacajawea had told them led toward the Shoshoni. Early the next morning they saw an Indian, riding bareback, on a magnificent horse. A Shoshoni at last!

Lewis unrolled his blanket and waved it in the signal of friendship. But the Indian galloped off.

Lewis was sure Indians were watching them. He tied a flag to a stick. They carried it high as they went on. When they camped, he left a mirror and beads tied to a tree for the Indians to find. Surely they would know that only friends would leave such fine gifts.

The stream they were following became a narrow brook. The brook ended in a clear, bubbling spring. The men stepped back and forth over the little brook and yelled like boys. To think they could step across the mighty Missouri!

"At last, I have done one of the things I have been determined to do as long as I can remember," said Lewis. "I have traced the Missouri 3,000 miles to its source."

They went on through a mountain pass. Ahead of them towering, snow-capped mountains stretched as far as they could see. On the steep mountainside they found a brook flowing west. Someday its water would reach the Pacific Ocean. Behind them all water flowed east to the Atlantic Ocean.

They had crossed the Continental Divide.

"Now we are beyond the Louisiana Territory," said Lewis. "All the land between here and the Pacific Ocean is unowned. We will claim it for the United States if we can find the Columbia River and travel down it before the British."

The next morning they saw a man, two women, and some dogs. Lewis went toward them waving the flag and calling "Ta-ba-bone." But the Indians ran away.

"No wonder other tribes say the Shoshoni vanish like spirits," said Lewis.

Then, as they climbed over the top of a gully, they were suddenly face to face with three Indian women. The frightened women dropped to their knees. They bent their heads for the death blow they expected.

One woman was very old. Lewis raised her gently to her feet. He pointed to the white skin of his upper arm. "Ta-ba-bone," he said. He painted their faces with red paint and gave them presents of beads and mirrors.

Suddenly there was a thunder of hoofs.

Sixty warriors on fiery horses galloped up in a rolling cloud of dust. The chief raced ahead of the others. He pulled up sharply and spoke to the women. Happily they showed him their presents.

The Chief leaped from his horse and ran toward Lewis shouting, "Ah-hi-e, ah-hi-e!"

He put his left arm around Lewis's right shoulder, and rubbed his cheeks against Lewis's. He greeted the others the same way. All the warriors did the same. Soon the faces of the white men were as paint-smeared as those of the Shoshoni.

"I was heartily tired of the national hug," Lewis wrote later. But he was very happy. They had found the Shoshoni at last.

CHAPTER 11

Sacajawea's Loyalty

"We are seeking a path over the mountains," Lewis told Cameahwait (*kay mee' ah wait*), the Shoshoni chief. "We need horses and guides. We have many good things to trade for them. My brother chief and other white men are bringing them up the river that flows to the buffalo plains. If you will go there with me, you will see them. A Shoshoni woman is with them. She will tell you I speak the truth."

Cameahwait was willing to go. Many warriors were not. That spring, enemies had killed twenty of their tribe and stolen many horses. How did they know these strangers would not lead them into a trap?

Lewis knew he *must* say the right thing.

He knew a warrior would do almost anything to prove his courage. "There must be some warriors brave enough to go with me and see that I speak the truth," he said. "Are Shoshoni warriors cowards? Are you afraid to die?"

"I am not afraid," said Cameahwait. But only a few warriors started back with them. They had not gone far when a dozen more galloped up. Soon most of the tribe was following.

Lewis sent Drewyer ahead to hunt. Suspicious braves followed him. Soon one of them raced back toward the party. He shouted something, wheeled his horse, and raced ahead again. The other Indians dashed after him, whipping their horses into a wild stampede.

When Lewis caught up, he found Drewyer cleaning a deer he had killed. He had tossed aside the bloody entrails. The Indians were eating them raw as fast as they could stuff them into their mouths.

The sight turned Lewis's stomach. But he

was filled with pity. Only people who had been terribly hungry for a long time would eat like that.

He knew, too, that they might easily have taken the whole deer. But they obeyed the law of the tribe — the kill belonged to the hunter. He gave them most of that deer and two others Drewyer killed later. It was the first time in a long time that the Shoshoni had had enough to eat.

As they neared the place where they were to meet Clark, Cameahwait put his fur tippet around Lewis's neck. He rubbed his cheeks against Lewis's until they were as paint-smeared as his own.

Lewis realized Cameahwait wanted him to be taken for a Shoshoni in case of a trap. Instantly he traded his cocked hat for Cameahwait's feathered headdress.

When they came to the place where the Jefferson divided, there was no sign of Clark's party. Some of the Indians half-turned to go back.

Lewis knew he would never find them again

if they left. There would be no horses. The expedition would fail. Desperately he handed his gun to Cameahwait. "Shoot me if you find I have betrayed you," he said.

He knew the uneasy Indians would not wait long. He wrote Clark a note. It said, "Hurry!" When Drewyer started down the Jefferson with it, stern silent warriors followed him.

The next morning Sacajawea was walking slowly along the river bank. How she wished she could run on ahead! Dragging the canoes up the twisting Jefferson had taken so long, and she was so eager to see her own people.

"Sometimes I don't think I'll *ever* see the Shoshoni again," she thought impatiently.

But she did — the very next minute!

Looking ahead she saw a party of Indians. Suddenly she was leaping and whirling in the "joy dance." Around and around she whirled. Pompey, tucked in his cradleboard, gave a surprised little squeal.

Clark and Charbonneau were close behind Sacajawea. She saw their startled faces.

Putting her fingers in her mouth she pointed to the approaching Indians. That was the Shoshoni sign for "my people."

As they came back up the river with Clark's party, the Shoshoni warriors started a joyful chant that echoed through the mountains. When they came near the meeting place, the tribe was waiting to greet them.

Suddenly Sacajawea felt shy. She had been only a child when she was captured. There were none of her own blanket left. Would anyone remember her?

At that moment a young woman darted ahead of the waiting warriors.

"Sacajawea!" she cried. "It is I, Red Plume. You have kept your word. You have returned!"

Other women ran to them. In a twinkling Sacajawea was almost hidden by a laughing, chattering group.

Clark and the others went on to where Lewis and Cameahwait waited. Soon they were all well smeared with grease from Shoshoni hugs.

When they formed the council circle, Cameahwait seated Clark on a white robe beside him. He tied six precious seashells in Clark's hair.

"I give you my own name, Cameahwait, as a sign of brotherhood," he said.

Indians and white men sat down together. The peace pipe went around. Finally the council could really begin. Lewis sent for Sacajawea.

Sacajawea came in with her eyes cast down. This was proper for a woman in the presence of great chiefs and mighty warriors. Clark made a speech. As Sacajawea opened her mouth to repeat his words she looked up at Cameahwait.

She stared. Her mouth stayed open, but no words came out. Then with a wild cry, "Little Bear! Brother!" she rushed into his arms.

There were tears in Cameahwait's eyes as he held her close.

It was some time before the council could go on. But the men did not mind. They

were all happy for Sacajawea. When she sat at Cameahwait's feet again, tears still slipped down her face. But they were tears of happiness.

"Are there any rivers by which our canoes can travel through the mountains to the west and on to the Bitter-Shoreless-Lake?" asked Lewis.

"No," said Cameahwait. "There are only wild, rock-filled mountain streams. I have heard that, far to the west, a mighty river flows to the Bitter-Shoreless-Lake. But it lies many suns' journey over a terrible mountain pass."

The Captains were sure that river was the Columbia. They asked Cameahwait for guides and horses.

"None of my people has ever been to that river," said Cameahwait. "But I will send for an old man of another tribe. He crossed the mountains to the west when he was a young brave."

"We cannot spare many horses," he went on. "But we will lend you horses to take you to friendly tribes nearby who have horses to sell."

After the council Cameahwait said to Sacajawea, "Little Sister, are the white men to be trusted?"

"Yes," said Sacajawea. "For many moons I have listened and watched. They say the same words to each chief. Always, *always,* they keep their word."

"It is a strange idea they have — for all tribes to live in peace," said Cameahwait.

"The Captains say all tribes are *Americans* now," said Sacajawea. "So it is the same as Storyteller said: 'Those of one tribe must live in peace together.' "

It made Sacajawea sad to see how poor and hungry her people were. She thought of the great stores of food and hides in the Hidatsa and Mandan lodges. Guns made the difference. If the Shoshoni had guns they, too, could live and hunt where there was plenty of food.

The Captains had said, "After we return to our own country many white men will

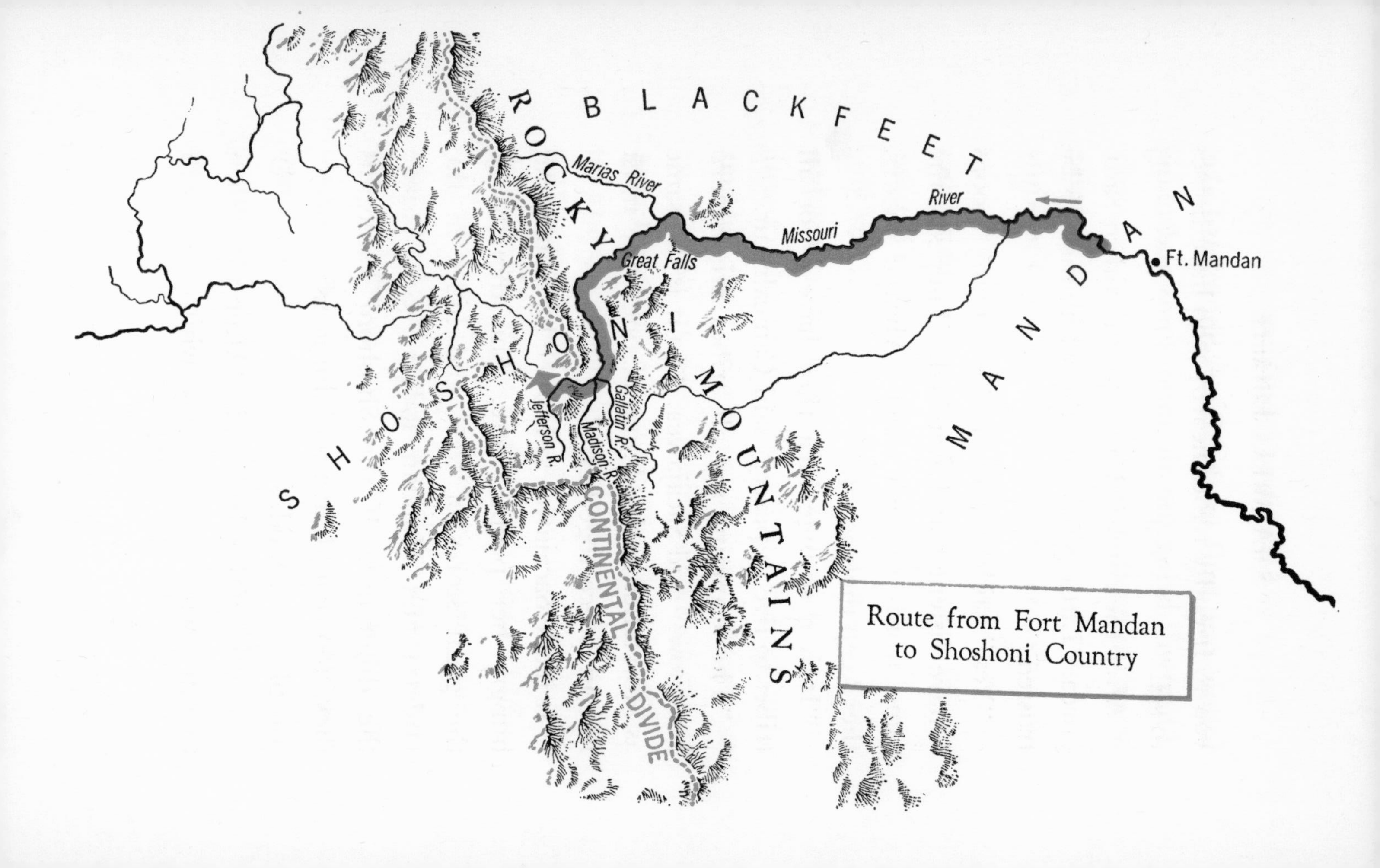

Route from Fort Mandan to Shoshoni Country

follow our trail to the Bitter-Shoreless-Lake. They will bring the Shoshoni guns and many other things they need."

"Guardian Spirit," she whispered, "please, help us make the journey swiftly so the white men will come soon."

The men had much work to do before they could start over the mountains. They repaired their tools and weapons. They dug another cache for everything they could possibly spare. They weighted the canoes with stones and sank them in the river. There they would be safe from floods and fires.

One day Sacajawea discovered that Cameahwait had ordered the Shoshoni to start for the buffalo plains the next morning. That would mean the expedition would be left without horses or guides.

Sacajawea did not know what to do. Should she be loyal to her brother or the Captains?

She loved Cameahwait dearly. She knew he would not break his word without a strong reason.

But Captain Clark had saved her life — and Pompey's. Even more important, if the Captains did not find a way to the Bitter-Shoreless-Lake, the white men would not come with guns for the Shoshoni.

"I am a Shoshoni," she thought, "but I am an American, too. I will warn the Captains."

Lewis went straight to Cameahwait. "Why did you break your promise?" he asked.

"My people are hungry," said Cameahwait simply. "They have been hungry for a long time. It is already late for the buffalo hunt. If we are too late and kill only a few buffalo, many of my people will starve during the winter."

"We trusted the word of a Shoshoni chief," said Lewis.

Cameahwait was silent for a long time. It was hard for him to choose between his hungry people and his promise to the white men.

At last he said, "I was wrong to break my word. I will do all that I promised."

Later, Lewis said to Clark, "I wonder how many 'civilized' rulers would risk the safety and comfort of their people for a few strangers?"

CHAPTER 12

Beyond the Shining Mountains

In September, Old Toby, the guide, pointed toward the clouds that hid the towering snow-covered peaks.

"Pass," he said.

"Looks as though we'll need wings instead of horses," said Cruzatte.

As they climbed the steep slopes, they hacked their way through thick brush. They crawled over rocks and fallen trees. They struggled up ridges so steep that horses slipped and rolled down the mountain side.

They climbed on through icy rain that turned to hail, then to sleet. Their clothes were soaked. Their feet were numb with cold. The skins around Pompey's cradle-board froze in stiff ridges.

It started to snow, and kept on. As they struggled around one peak, they saw rows of silent white peaks ahead. The world they knew disappeared. They had only the memory of an old, old Indian to guide them.

Day after day the hunters came back empty-handed. They used all their flour and dried corn. They ate thin, watery "portable" soup. One day Drewyer shot a crow. The men cheered, "Meat for the soup!" Then the soup was gone.

Their clothing hung on their thin bodies like ragged sacks. Scannon was a bundle of fur and bones.

One night dinner was a quart of melted bear's fat and twenty melted tallow candles. The next night they shivered, supperless, around the campfire.

Suddenly Scannon ran off into the dusk, barking wildly. Lewis followed him. A wolf was creeping toward the horses. Lewis took careful aim . . .

Dinner was wolf stew. Scannon had praise, pats, and all the bones.

They went without food for a day. Weakness made the men move slowly and awkwardly. Even mighty York strained at logs which he could ordinarily move with only one hand.

"We must have food," said Lewis, "or we will die in these cursed mountains." He ordered a horse killed for dinner. The men ate heartily.

But Sacajawea said, "No. The Shoshoni do not eat the flesh of animals that work for them." She chewed bark and tree shoots as the horses did.

They climbed on through clouds that hid the canyons below and the peaks ahead. They crawled around narrow ledges on their hands and knees.

They killed and ate two more horses. It meant heavier loads for the other horses — and the men. Two horses gave out.

Some of the men could hardly walk for coughing. Clark sprained his hip. Lewis had a fever. Still there was no end to the savage peaks ahead.

Sometimes each of the Captains wondered if their little party would live through the nightmare of the mountains.

One morning they crept around a ledge so narrow the horses' packs hung over empty air for a thousand feet. Suddenly they realized the ledge sloped *down!* Only a little — but *down!*

Then, through a hole in the clouds, they saw a wide green valley far below.

The trail was still rough and hard but it *seemed* easier. Sliding, stumbling, and slipping, they scrambled down the mountain side, through the brush and timber of the foothills, to the green valley.

For the first time Americans had crossed the Rocky Mountains!

Friendly Nez Percé Indians brought them dried salmon and camass roots. They ate until they all had terrible stomach-aches from stuffing themselves so soon after nearly starving.

The Captains asked Twisted Hair, the Nez Percé chief, if he knew of a river which flowed to the Bitter-Shoreless-Lake.

"Yes," he said. He pointed to the river flowing through the valley. "That river (the Clearwater) flows into a bigger river (the Snake). That, in turn, flows into the mighty river you seek (the Columbia)."

Now they could travel by water again. They made five dugout canoes. They branded their horses and left them in the care of Twisted Hair's tribe.

On October 7, they climbed into the canoes and were on their way again.

All the way up the Missouri they had fought against the current. Now they were traveling downstream. The banks whizzed by. The men yelled and shouted. The canoes raced each other. They traveled thirty and forty miles a day.

Sacajawea loved to ride in the front of a skimming canoe. The wind and spray and the swiftly passing shore made her feel as if she were flying. When the Indians saw her,

with Pompey on her back, they were not afraid of the strangers. In that region a woman with a party of men was a sign of peace. When the Captains learned this, they made sure Sacajawea was always in one of the first canoes.

On October 16, they swept into the Columbia River. They had come 3,721 miles from the mouth of the Missouri.

The Columbia was filled with silver salmon. To the tribes along the river the salmon was as important as the buffalo to the tribes of the Great Plains. There were drying racks, loaded with salmon, in every village they passed.

The Indians along the Columbia were no more like the Indians east of the Rockies than a salmon is like a buffalo. They were a short, plump, bowlegged people who spoke a queer gurgling language.

They strapped their babies' foreheads between two boards. In time their foreheads grew in one straight line from the end of their nose to the top of their peaked little heads.

They were not warlike, but many of them were greedy and dishonest.

There were so many villages that the Captains could not stop to hold councils in each one. Besides, they soon had another reason for not going into the Indian lodges. In fact, hundreds of lively reasons — fleas!

The fleas leaped happily from the Indians

to the white men — where they were less crowded. The men slapped, scratched, and stripped to the skin to brush them off.

"I wouldn't mind their chawing on me so much," said Cruzatte, scratching and squirming, "but they keep me awake chomping their teeth and smacking their lips."

As the Columbia cut through the Cascade Mountains it poured over a waterfall twenty feet high. The Captains rented horses from the Indians and portaged around it.

Then, for many miles the water boiled and billowed through narrow, twisting canyons and raced over foaming, rock-filled rapids.

To portage the heavy canoes around this stretch would take a long time. Cruzatte studied the water in the canyons carefully.

"Any good Missouri voyageur can 'shoot' that," he said.

They unloaded the canoes. Those who could not swim walked and carried the baggage. The others brought the canoes safely through.

One morning an Indian glided past in a

light canoe that was different from those of the tribes above the falls. He wore a sailor's jacket. A round sailor's hat was perched jauntily on his little peaked head.

That jacket and hat could only have come from sailors of ships that traded along the Pacific coast. They *must* be near the Pacific.

On November 7, they were paddling through cold rain and thick fog. Suddenly the fog lifted and the sun shone brightly for a moment. Looking ahead Sacajawea saw a great body of blue-green water with tossing white-capped waves. "Look!" she cried.

"Hurrah!" shouted the men.

Clark took out a notebook. "Ocian in view! O! the joy," he wrote.

The fog closed down again and a raging storm whipped the water into great waves. The heavy dugout canoes were not meant for cliff-like waves. They lurched up and plunged down.

Sacajawea's stomach felt very odd. The men turned a strange coppery-green.

Rocky cliffs rose straight from the water.

It seemed like years before they found a narrow beach and crawled ashore.

"Land!" said Joe Fields. "Firm, dry land!"

But it wasn't dry. There was no shelter from the rain. The hurricane-like wind drove huge waves foaming and hissing across the narrow beach.

When they tried to leave, the wild sea drove them back. It was six wet, miserable days before they could paddle on to a new campsite.

The Indians told the Captains that any trading ships which came up the coast anchored in a nearby bay.

The Captains, and many of the men, cut their names, the date, and the words, "By land from the United States in 1804 and 1805," on trees growing around the bay.

Their journey had established the claim of the United States to the whole Columbia River Basin. They wanted to leave a record where it might be found by sailors of all nations.

The wet, ragged men did not think of themselves as heroes. They would have howled with laughter at the idea. Who ever heard of heroes with shaggy beards, sore feet, and tattered buckskin clothes?

They had simply set out to reach the Pacific Ocean by land. They had done so.

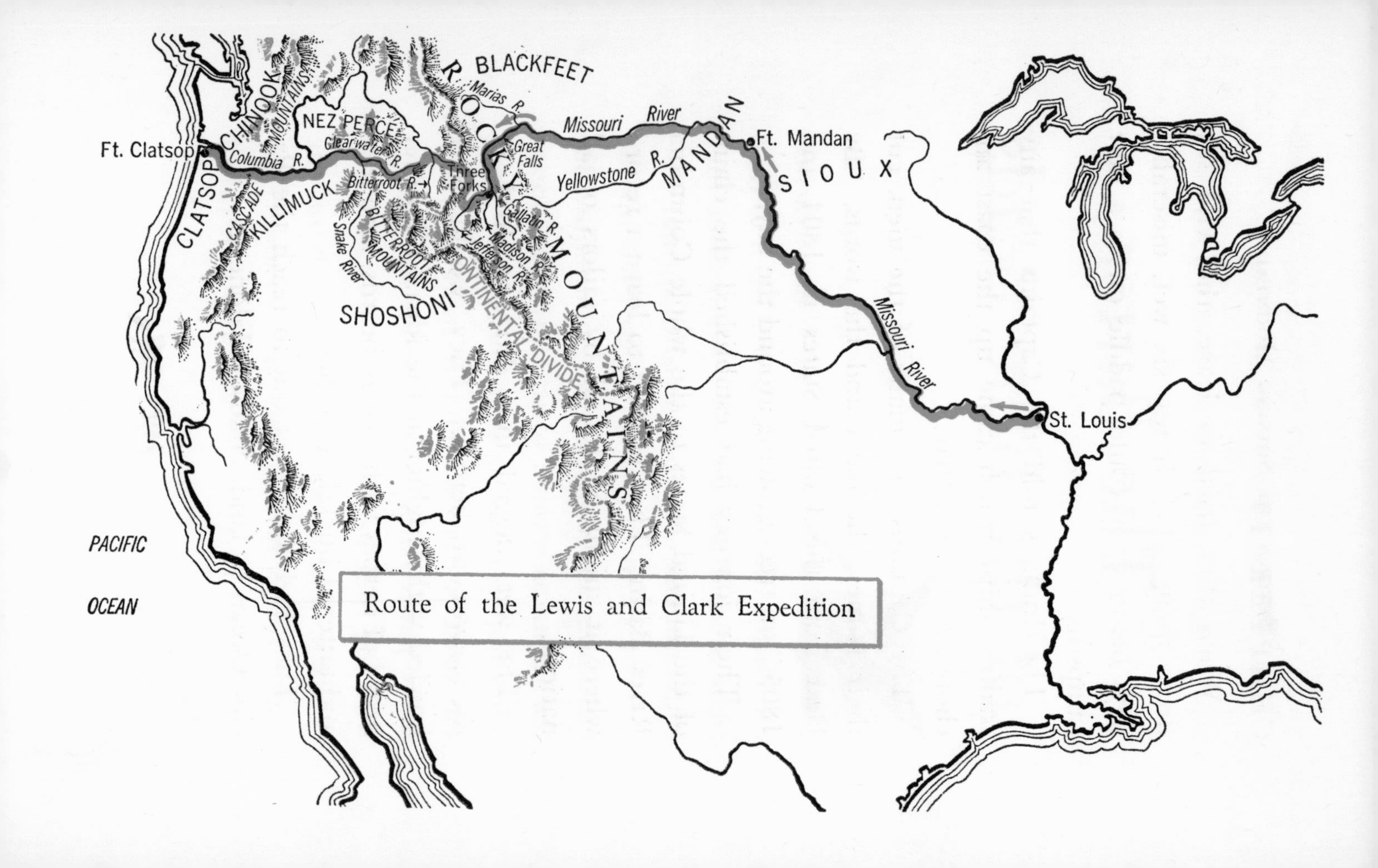

Route of the Lewis and Clark Expedition

CHAPTER 13

The Barter of the Blue Beads

Now that they had reached the Pacific, the men would have liked to turn right around and go home again. But they could not cross the Rockies until spring.

Some of them wanted to go back up the Columbia and wait near the mountains. But the Captains wanted to stay near the ocean. They hoped a trading ship would come along the coast so they could buy more supplies. They particularly needed goods for trading with the Indians.

Clark did not want to be directly on the coast. "The ocean roars like thunder day and night," he said. "It should not be called 'Pacific.' "

They built the winter fort a few miles back from the coast.

Rain pelted and poured while the men cut down trees. It sprinkled and showered while they sawed them into logs. It dripped and drizzled while they heaved the heavy logs into place.

The fort was a fifty-foot square, with seven snug cabins inside the log stockade. They named it Fort Clatsop, after friendly Indians nearby.

They moved in on Christmas Eve. For the first time since leaving Fort Mandan they slept under a roof.

Next morning, as the first gray light crept into the sky, there was a sudden burst of gunfire.

The Captains leaped from their bunks, grabbed their rifles, and jerked open their cabin door in one motion.

"Merry Christmas!" shouted the men gathered outside. They laughed at the Captains' astonished faces.

Then everyone stood at attention while

the flag was raised over the fort for the first time.

The Captains gave each other socks and underwear. There was tobacco for the men who smoked and a handkerchief apiece for the others. The men gave the Captains small gifts they had made.

Then Sacajawea astonished everyone. All year she had remembered this great feast day of the white men. For months she had been planning a surprise. Her eyes sparkled with excitement as she laid a small skin-wrapped bundle in front of the Captains. Inside were two dozen black-tipped, white ermine tails. They were fine enough for even such great chiefs as Lewis and Clark.

There had been no time for hunting while they built the fort. Christmas dinner was only spoiled elk meat, dried fish, and wappato roots. But they drank toasts in water and pretended it was a feast.

Cruzatte brought out his fiddle and played his liveliest tunes. Pompey held tight to Clark's big hand and moved his tiny moccasined feet in time to the gay music.

The men were warm and dry. Today, for the first time, an American flag had flown over a fort on the Pacific coast. Christmas was merry in little Fort Clatsop, four thousand miles from the mouth of the Missouri.

Everyone was busy. The hunters went out every day. Any meat they did not eat was dried. The hides were made into clothes. The fat was molded into candles.

Five of the men set up a salt camp on the beach. They made fine white salt by boiling sea water in big kettles.

One day the salt makers brought a strange new food to the fort. It looked like salt pork and tasted like beaver. It was blubber from a huge whale that had washed up on the shore.

"It's a hundred and five feet long," said Joe Fields. "More than twice as long as the fort."

"How I would like to see the great fish!" thought Sacajawea. "How I wish Pompey could see it!" When Clark decided to go after more blubber, she begged to go along. She had never before asked anything for herself.

"Such a reasonable request cannot be denied," said Clark with a smile.

They found only the skeleton of the huge sea beast. The Indians had stripped off every bit of the flesh.

Sacajawea walked around and around the monstrous bones, staring with wide eyes.

Who would have believed there was a fish big enough to swallow a tepee?

She looked far out over the dancing blue-green water to the place where sky and water met.

"I am the first woman of my tribe ever to follow the setting sun to the place where the land ends," she thought. "How lucky I am to have seen such wonders. Truly, my guardian spirit has guided my moccasins."

The Captains wrote in their journals every day. Clark drew many maps. Lewis wrote about the Clatsops, Chinooks, Killimucks, and other nearby Indian tribes.

To the Pacific Coast tribes the dark glossy skin of the sea otter was the most valuable of all furs. One day an Indian came to the fort wearing a robe made of two magnificent sea otter skins.

The Captains thought it would make a wonderful addition to their collection of articles for President Jefferson. They tried to buy it.

They offered the best articles in their small

stock of trade goods. The Indian laughed. Clark offered a silver dollar and his pocket compass. The answer was, "No." Lewis added a pair of his own shiny satin knee breeches. The Indian sneered. Slowly Clark held out his watch. "No." Then Lewis offered his best lace and gold-braid-trimmed uniform coat. The Indian shook his head.

The Captains gave up. They had nothing more to offer.

Sacajawea did not understand why the collection for President Jefferson was so important to them. But she knew it had something to do with being an American. She also knew they must want the robe *very* much. They had offered their own most treasured possessions for it.

"I am an American, too," she thought. "And *I* know what the tribes who live by the Bitter-Shoreless-Lake want most. Surely this is the time of my mother's dream."

Slowly she took off her blue bead belt. She held it out carefully so it sparkled and gleamed in the firelight.

The Indian's black eyes snapped. Here were shimmering blue chief beads such as he had never seen before. The sea was full of otters.

He tossed the robe to Clark, grabbed the belt, and ran before the crazy squaw could change her mind.

When the astonished Captains tried to thank Sacajawea, she nodded gravely. She did not know how to tell them she had only been loyal to her people — the Americans.

In March they made ready for the long trip back. All winter they had kept a lookout posted to watch for a ship. But no ship had come.

"Two handkerchiefs will hold all our small articles of merchandise," said Lewis grimly. It would have to do.

Often, during the winter, the men had cut their names and the date on trees along the coast. Now, Lewis wrote out a statement of the dates on which they had left St. Louis and reached the Pacific coast. He listed the names of the men. Clark added a map of their route to prove they had explored the Columbia from the Rockies to the Pacific Ocean. They nailed it to the wall of their office. They gave copies to friendly chiefs.

"I hope that somehow this statement may reach the eyes of a civilized person," said Lewis.

On March 23, 1806, the party climbed into the canoes and started back to the United States.

The Indians along the lower part of the river were sulky and spiteful. They jeered at the white men who were so poor in trade goods. They stole everything that wasn't nailed down or guarded carefully. Small articles vanished like smoke.

The Captains were patient until Scannon was stolen. Then Lewis's patience snapped. He sent three men racing after the thieves.

"Fire if they do not give you Scannon, *instantly!*" he commanded.

When the thieves saw the grim-looking men with their guns ready, they let Scannon go and ran. Scannon bounded back to Lewis, barking happily. Lewis patted him.

"The next man we find stealing will be killed!" he told the Indians. There was no doubt that he meant *exactly* what he said.

The Columbia was in spring flood. Paddling upstream in the heavy dugouts was painfully slow and hard. Even York's great strength was no match for the flood-swollen current. The Captains decided to trade the canoes for horses and travel back to the Rockies by land.

The greedy Indians drove hard bargains. The party finally got a few horses by trading the canoes, their cooking kettles, the Captains' uniforms and cocked hats, and even the buttons from their clothes.

They were all glad when they were finally beyond the Indian tribes who lived near the Pacific coast.

But they were still thousands of miles from home. They needed to buy more horses and other things from the Indians. All their trade goods were gone. What could they do?

CHAPTER 14

White Medicine Men

Once more it was Sacajawea who saved them.

The wife of a chief had a sore back. Sacajawea told her the Captains were powerful medicine men — great healers. She told how they had cured her when she was sick.

The chief promised the Captains a horse if they could cure his wife.

Clark rubbed her back with liniment and put a warm cloth over the sore spot. Soon the woman said happily that the pain was gone. The chief gave them a fine horse.

From then on the Captains were "medicine men."

The news flew up the river ahead of them.

A line of patients waited at every village. Many of the Indians had sore eyes. The Captains gave them soothing eye-water. They also set broken bones, rubbed aches with liniment, and washed dirty sores with clean water and soap. Some of their "cures" surprised even the Captains.

Their grateful patients brought them horses, food, and other things they needed.

They had so many patients their supply of medicine began to run low — especially the eye-water.

"I can brew a medicine that will help sore eyes," Sacajawea said to Clark. She told him of the secrets Mi-he-wi had taught her.

Clark remembered the root which drew the poison from the rattlesnake's bite. Their own medicine would soon be gone. He decided he would try Sacajawea's remedy.

Sacajawea secretly gathered the herbs. She brewed the eye-water just as Mi-he-wi had taught her. It seemed to work as well as the Captains'. They did not tell anyone there had been a change in prescriptions. There were just as many cures as there were before.

Early in May they reached the Nez Percé village where they had left their horses. The snow-capped Rockies towered just beyond.

The Indians said, "You cannot cross the mountains before the next full moon. The snow is still too deep."

They camped in a wide green valley where there was plenty of fish and game.

One morning Pompey was very sick. Sacajawea took him to Clark. "Please make him well," she said.

Clark loved Pompey dearly. "If only I were a real doctor," he thought when he saw Pompey's flushed face and red, swollen throat.

He tried all their medicines. He sent men into the high plains for wild onions to make a poultice. When Pompey fought for breath, Clark went without sleep to hold him in his arms. At last the terrible swelling grew less. The fever went down. Pompey smiled weakly at the toys the men made for him. Soon he was holding tightly to Clark's finger and trotting about the camp again.

Of course Sacajawea was happy, but she had never doubted for a minute that Clark could cure Pompey.

In June the Indians said, "Wait a little longer. The snow in the passes is still deeper than the head of a man on horseback."

It was hot in the valley. From there the snow looked like delicate white frosting. The men were strong, rested — and homesick. Why should they wait?

On June 11, they started across the Rockies. The snow had a crust of ice that was firm enough to walk on. But it grew deeper and deeper until they walked beside the tops of trees. Soon all the marks of the trail were hidden.

"If we lose our way in this trackless wilderness we will leave our bones in these mountains," said Lewis. "Then all our discoveries will be lost to the United States."

"It would be madness to go on," Clark agreed. "Better to turn back now while men and horses are still fresh."

For the first time the party turned back.

On June 24 they started over the mountains again with three Nez Percé braves leading the way.

Their guides led them surely and swiftly across bleak ridges and around gaunt cliffs. The rocks and fallen trees they had struggled over in the fall were buried deep under the hard-crusted snow. They crossed one hundred and fifty-six miles of the Rocky Mountains in six days.

They camped in a pleasant valley to plan the three-thousand-mile trip ahead. Here the Captains made a bold decision.

They must travel fast to reach St. Louis before winter. But the Captains thought it was their duty to explore as much of the West as they could. By splitting the party they could explore new routes without taking more time.

They decided that Lewis, with a few men and the swiftest horses, would travel north to find the source of the Marias River. Then they would follow the river back to the Missouri.

Clark and the others would go to the place where the Jefferson divided for the canoes and baggage.

From there Sergeant Ordway and nine men would take the canoes down the Jefferson to the Three Forks, and then down the Missouri to the mouth of the Marias River. There they would meet Lewis and his party.

Clark and the others, with the rest of the horses, would travel east to the Yellowstone River. They would follow it to the Missouri. They would meet Lewis and the others where the Yellowstone entered the Missouri.

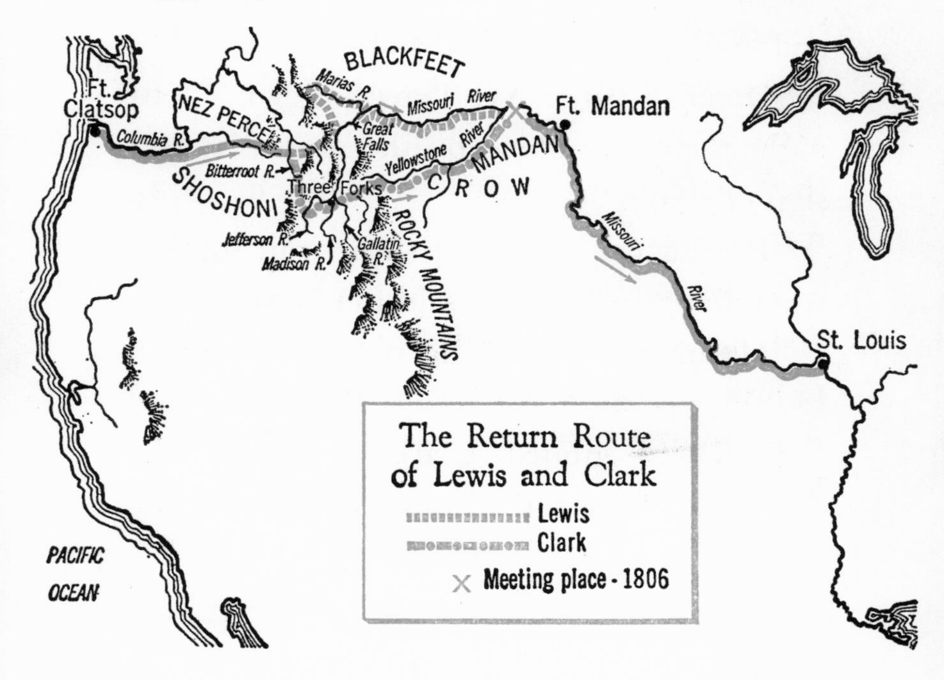

The men of the expedition had worked as a team for over two years. They were all sure the plan would work perfectly. But the Nez Percé guides beat their hands against their foreheads.

"You have been safe from attack only because you are a large party," they said. "It is dangerous to split into small groups!

"Especially for you," they told Lewis. "You plan to go into the very heart of the Blackfoot country. They are the fiercest, most treacherous of all the Plains tribes."

But the Captains were determined to carry out their plan. Next morning at dawn Lewis and his men saddled their horses.

"Don't go," the Nez Percé begged. "Last night there was blood on the moon. It is a sign of death."

"Danger does not keep American soldiers from doing their duty," said Lewis sternly.

"Mount and ride!" he ordered, and galloped off.

Sacajawea guided Clark's party to the Jefferson. It was the country of her childhood. She knew every valley and pass. She remembered the line of every peak against the sky.

At the Jefferson they dug up the cache and raised the sunken canoes. Sergeant Ordway and his men took them down the river as they had planned.

Clark and the others, with Sacajawea and Pompey, rode on into the beautiful valley of the Yellowstone.

The weather was fine. There was plenty of game. Wildflowers scented the air. Wild grapes and berries hung in sweet ripe clusters. Life was perfect.

Then Sacajawea pointed to dark puffs of smoke floating up from a distant hill.

"Crow Indians," she said. "No other tribe is so clever at stealing horses. They plan to steal ours."

The men took extra care, but one morning half the horses were gone. The Crows had taken them away over hard, stony ground so they left no trail.

Clark knew the Indians looked on horse

stealing as a "sport." He did not want to play games with the thieving Crows. He told Sergeant Pryor and three men to take the rest of the horses across country to the Mandan village.

The others made two dugout canoes. Traveling down the swift-flowing Yellowstone was fast, easy, and fun. Pompey had a "special" seat on Clark's lap. He nodded happily as Clark pointed out grizzlies swimming in the icy river, herds of grazing elk and buffalo, and beavers building dams.

Gaily the party named the rivers they passed.

"Let's call this one Clark's Fork," shouted the men as they passed one of the streams.

Clark swept off his coonskin hat and made a gallant bow. "Thank you, gentlemen." Pompey laughed and clapped his hands because everyone else was in such a fine humor.

Sometimes they landed to stretch, and hunt, and do a little sightseeing.

One day they saw a tall column of rock

where the Indians had carved hundreds of pictures. Clark swung Pompey to his shoulder and strode over for a closer look. He took out his knife and added his name and the date — July 25, 1806.

"We'll call this 'Pompey's Pillar' after Pompey," he said.

On August 3, plump with good food and little work, they reached the Missouri.

They camped on the low, marshy ground where the two rivers met. There they were attacked by a fierce enemy — mosquitoes. Even at noon they were thick as fog. The men could neither work nor sleep. Pompey's face was swollen round and red as a balloon.

Clark left a note for Lewis tied to a pole on the river bank. They paddled on down the Missouri until they found a high dry spot for a camp.

On August 12, Lewis's party came down the river. They shouted and yelled as they sighted Clark's camp and pulled into shore.

Everyone rushed to greet them. The men in camp saw all their friends were climbing out safe and sound — except — where was Captain Lewis?

Then Lewis raised himself weakly from the bottom of a canoe. Cruzatte had accidentally shot him in the thigh. It was only a flesh wound, painful, but not serious.

That night everyone sat late around the campfire listening to the story of the men who had explored along the Marias river.

CHAPTER 15

A Race for Life

"As we rode north," Lewis began, "we kept a sharp watch for the bloodthirsty Blackfeet. But we saw only wolves, buffalo, and wild horses. One day we saw a wounded buffalo. That meant Indians nearby. We were even more watchful. But we traveled to the mountains, where the Marias begins, without seeing a single Indian.

"We started back down the Marias to the Missouri. Late one afternoon Drewyer was riding along the river valley. The Fields and I were riding along the bluffs above. Coming to the top of a hill we saw eight Blackfoot warriors watching Drewyer.

"It was a very unpleasant sight," Lewis added.

The men around the campfire looked

grim. Four men against a party of Blackfoot warriors . . .

Lewis decided on a bold approach. "Our orders are to make friends with the Indians," he told the Fields. "We will be friendly unless they force us to be otherwise. In that case they must find that the soldiers of the United States Army can, and will, fight to the death."

The Fields nodded grimly. They rode forward with their American flag waving gallantly in the breeze.

When the Blackfeet saw them, they galloped toward them at full speed. A short distance away they stopped. One Indian rode on alone. Lewis ordered the Fields to stop. He rode to meet the lone Indian and shook his hand. Then he went on and shook hands with the others. He saw that only two had guns. The rest had bows and arrows.

The Indians asked to smoke with the white men. Lewis had been wondering how to reach Drewyer. This was his chance.

"The white warrior by the river has my

pipe," he said. "I will send for him."

It would soon be night. "If we separate now, the Blackfeet might ambush us in the darkness," Lewis told his men. "It is better to have them where we can watch them."

"Let us camp together so we can smoke and talk," he said to the Indians.

The Indians agreed. Three of them said they were chiefs. Lewis gave one a flag, one a handkerchief, and one a peace medal. He kept them smoking and talking late. Finally they all went to sleep.

Reuben Fields was standing guard. Before Lewis lay down he told him, "Waken us instantly if any Indian leaves camp." But the Indians lay quietly all night.

Just at dawn a stealthy hand slipped Drewyer's rifle from under his blanket. Drewyer grabbed it as it moved.

"Let go of my gun!" he yelled.

Lewis grabbed for his gun. It was gone. He saw an Indian running off with it. Drawing his pistol Lewis raced after him. "Drop that gun!" he shouted.

Another Indian snatched up the Fields' rifles and ran. They sprinted after him. The Indian turned and swung a rifle at Joe's head. Joe dodged. Reuben leaped on the thief and drove his hunting knife into his heart. It was the chief to whom Lewis had given the peace medal. The Fields snatched up their rifles and ran toward the thief who had Lewis's gun. He dropped it as they came close.

"Hold fire!" shouted Lewis as he saw the

Fields's raised rifles. "He obeyed orders and he is unarmed."

Drewyer dragged up the Indian who had stolen his gun. "Shall I kill him, Captain," he asked, "so he can't play any more sneakin' Blackfoot tricks?"

"No," said Lewis sternly. "President Jefferson said to treat the natives in a friendly manner and avoid bloodshed."

Drewyer and the Fields looked at each other. These were *bad* Indians who did not believe in honor and fair play.

A minute later their unspoken thoughts were proved right. The Blackfeet had sneaked around to the white men's horses. Suddenly they started driving them off in two directions. Without horses Lewis and his men would never live to reach the Missouri.

"Stop them!" shouted Lewis. "Shoot if you must!"

Drewyer and the Fields chased six Indians who were driving most of the horses up the river. Lewis ran after the two who were driving the rest of the horses the other way.

He ran until his heart hammered in his chest and a red mist swam before his eyes.

"Stop!" he shouted, "or I'll fire!"

One Indian jumped behind a rock. The other whirled and raised his own gun, aiming it at Lewis.

Lewis fired. The Indian fell, rolled over, and crawled behind a rock. He raised himself and fired. Lewis felt the wind of the bullet stir his hair.

Lewis was out of ammunition. He went back to camp. The flag he had given the Blackfeet was lying on the ground. Lewis picked it up. He started to take the peace medal from the neck of the dead chief. Then his face grew stern.

"I will leave it," he thought. "It will be a warning that the soldiers of the Great White Father punish those who disobey his command to live in peace."

The Fields brought back four horses.

"Every Blackfoot in the country will be after our scalps," said Joe Fields as they saddled them. "What's more, if they find Ordway and his men before we do, they'll massacre them."

"Smoke signals travel mighty fast," said Drewyer. "We'd better get to the Missouri *quick!*"

"Ride as you have never ridden before," Lewis ordered. Their horses were strong and fresh. By night they had made eighty miles. When they stopped to rest, Drewyer shot a buffalo. They ate the meat almost raw.

They rode on by moonlight. They galloped past great herds of sleepy buffalo, over creeks, through gullies, on and on . . .

At last they could go no further. They slid from their horses, dropped to the ground, and slept.

Lewis wakened with the first gray light of dawn. He called the men. They groaned as they tried to move their stiff muscles.

"Remember we are racing against death," said Lewis. "Our lives, and those of our friends, are the prize."

They mounted and rode on. As they galloped over the wide plains near the Missouri they crouched low in their saddles. Every second they expected to hear savage Blackfoot warhoops.

Their horses staggered with exhaustion as they climbed the steep river bluffs. From the top the men looked down fearfully. Then they yelled and whooped with joy. The white pirogue and the canoes were coming peacefully down the river. Both parties had reached the meeting place at the same time.

The men gave their horses a final pat and left them grazing contentedly on the prairie. Then they ran down the river bank and leaped into the canoes.

"Let's get out of here," Lewis shouted, "and let's get out fast!"

With flashing paddles they pushed out into the racing downstream current. Soon they were far beyond the country of the avenging Blackfeet.

They found Clark's note at the mouth of the Yellowstone and went on until they sighted his camp.

CHAPTER 16

The Sign Fulfilled

The next morning they went on down the Missouri. As they pulled into the shore below the Mandan village, yelling children, squealing squaws, shouting warriors, and barking dogs ran to greet them. Hands and arms flew like windmills in the sign language. The men did not need to understand the words to know they were being welcomed back. After the long lonely months in the wilderness, it was a fine feeling.

Chief Black Cat told them all the news of the tribes along the river. Many Indians who had promised the Captains to live peacefully had gone back to fighting as soon as they left.

"A war party of Minnetarees ambushed

the Shoshoni on their way to the buffalo plains, last fall," said Black Cat. "Many Shoshoni were killed. Among them was the chief. But, truly, it is as I told you. Only one who was part spirit could fight so fiercely. Armed only with a spear he took many great Minnetaree warriors to the Happy Hunting Grounds with him."

"Cameahwait was our friend," Clark told Sacajawea. "He was a brave warrior and a noble chief."

"He died as a Shoshoni chief should die," said Sacajawea proudly, "fighting for his people."

They stayed with the friendly Mandans three days. The last night the men gave a party with all their "star" acts. Cruzatte's fiddle fairly sang. York danced as if he had springs in his toes. Scannon begged, rolled over, and played dead.

But all the men were a little sad because the time had come to say good-by to Sacajawea, Pompey, and Charbonneau. Their home was near. They were staying here.

The next morning Sacajawea and Pompey stood on the bluffs watching the party go swiftly down the river. Pompey waved the bright flag he clutched in one hand.

"American!" he said clearly.

Sacajawea was startled. His first real word — and it was in English. Then she hugged him happily. Truly it was a sign from the spirits. Pompey was an *American!*

After they left the Mandans, the men felt as if they were almost home. Their paddles made quick shining circles in the swift downstream current. They often traveled sixty and seventy miles in one day. One morning they met a trader coming up the river.

"What's the news?" the men shouted.

"News?" The trader laughed. "Gentlemen, *you* are! The return of the Lewis and Clark Expedition will be the biggest news in the whole United States.

"Everyone thinks you were killed by savages in the Shining Mountains, or eaten by fire-breathing monsters in the wilderness. Only President Jefferson still believes that you live."

The men roared with laughter. How silly to think that they could not make such a simple journey safely!

Suddenly Lewis and Clark and the other men broke into joyful yells. Scannon almost went overboard barking. By the river stood an animal that seemed stranger to them than any monster of the wilderness — a yellow cow.

On September 23, 1806, they reached St. Louis. They had been gone 2 years, 4 months, and 12 days, and traveled over 8,000 miles.

Cheering people lined the riverbank. Cannons boomed in salute to the first Americans ever to cross the continent of North America and return.

"We succeeded because every member of our party did his full share," said Clark. "And no one deserves more credit than Sacajawea."

"Yes," Lewis agreed. "There was not a man in our party with more courage, determination, and patience. Without her loyalty and quick thinking the expedition might easily have failed."

"America will always owe her a great debt," said Clark, and Lewis agreed.

Author's Note

The Lewis and Clark Expedition took place a long time ago. But we know thousands of facts about it because the Captains kept a careful record. They wrote in their journals every day. Some of the men also kept journals.

They told what they thought, did, and said. They told what they ate — and how they liked it. They wrote of the weather, the country, and the Indians they met. They described trees, plants, animals, birds, fish, and insects.

All we know of Sacajawea is what was written in the journals. But we can fill in details of her childhood with what we know about the life of the Shoshoni Indians of that time.

Only a few of the important facts from the journals could be crammed into one small book. But I have tried to choose those which will give you a clear picture of the brave, loyal Indian girl and the courageous men who, with their faithful dog, were the first Americans to cross the Rocky Mountains and go on to the Pacific Ocean.

The story of the Lewis and Clark Expedition is a true story as exciting as any adventure story ever written.

JERRY SEIBERT